N

A HUNDRED YEARS OF EVOLUTION

Darwin, said Julian Huxley recently, was one of the greatest scientists the world has ever known : he gave us a completely new way of looking at the biological universe and revolutionised man's thinking about animals and, by extension, human affairs. Dr. Carter, a zoologist who has given much thought to evolution and written on the modern theory, here surveys the changes of thought that have taken place in the hundred years since the publication of " The Origin of Species," an event now being commemorated by the scientific world. The first part of his book is devoted to the nineteenth century and Dr. Carter traces the background of Darwin and the position in scientific and general thought ; the development of ideas concerning evolution ; and the reaction to " The Origin " among the general public as well as among biologists. Then turning to the twentieth century his chapters are on Mendel's experiments on inheritance ; genetics and ecology over the last thirty years ; and, finally, a consideration of the larger course of evolution.

It is a book the specialist will not find beneath his interest, and the author's mastery of his subject—always a popular one—ensures a fascinating text for the layman.

A HUNDRED YEARS OF

Evolution

BY

G. S. CARTER

Corpus Christi College Cambridge

NEW YORK

THE MACMILLAN COMPANY

1957

PRINTED IN GREAT BRITAIN BY
J. W. ARROWSMITH LTD., BRISTOL

What I like about experience is that it is such an honest thing. You may take any number of wrong turnings; but keep your eyes open and you will not be allowed to go very far before the warning signs appear. You may have deceived yourself, but experience is not trying to deceive you. The universe rings true wherever you fairly test it.

C. S. Lewis

PREFACE

WITHIN the compass of this short book it has not been possible to give more than a summary of the story of evolution theory in the last hundred years. I have had to leave out much that would deserve a place in a larger book, and to touch on, rather than discuss adequately, many of the aspects of the history that have been included. Yet a short and summary account such as this seems to be worth-while, for it may be hoped that the really significant episodes of the story will stand out in sharper focus in a short book.

There is, however, another disadvantage in compressing a long story into a short space. Where opinions differ, it is not always easy to set out every side of the argument shortly; the discussion tends towards a statement of personal opinion. I have tried to avoid this, and to give what seems to be the views most generally accepted today. But this, again, is not always easy. In discussion of an actively advancing subject, such as the study of evolution now is, it is often difficult to decide what is precisely the accepted position. Opinions are continually changing, advances are not always accepted at once, and out-of-date views are often held long after thay have been shown to be false. One cannot always be sure that the views one is expressing are those with which the majority of biologists would agree. To that extent one's account is bound to be personal. In any case, other books on the subject will be written in celebration of the centenary of Darwin's work, and I cannot hope that all will be in complete agreement with me. Some may view the position very differently.

In writing the book, my aim has been to give a summary of the subject that may be useful to the biologist who is not primarily interested in the theory of evolution, and may also be intelligible to the non-biological layman who wishes for some account of the development of thought on the problems of evolution. I have laid emphasis on discussion of the subject in relation to the development of non-biological thought through the century, for it seems to me that insistence on the interplay between the advances of science and thought of other kinds is needed at the present time, and the subject of evolution is an ideal one for such a treatment. For a biologist to wander from purely scientific discussion may seem rash. In extenuation I am glad to say that I have to thank my friend, Dr. J. P. C. Roach, for reading the manuscript from the historical point of view, and for saving me from many errors and suggesting many improvements. It is surely worth-while that the interactions between thought within science and outside it should be discussed, and it is not often that anyone will be found to discuss them whose interests are not predominantly on one side or the other. I have also to thank Dr. C. F. A. Pantin for reading the manuscript and for making valuable suggestions for its improvement, and Rev. R. C. Walls for reading the latter parts of Chapters 2 and 5. His help was also valuable.

I have given references only to sources that may be useful for further reading, not to the origins of all the information given.

I am indebted to Messrs. Macmillan & Co. for permission to reproduce Fig. 2 from "Recent Progress in the Study of Variation Heredity and Evolution" by R. H. Lock, and to the Macmillan Company of New York for permission to reproduce Fig. 3 from "A History of the Land Mammals of the Western Hemisphere" by W. B. Scott, copyright 1937 by the American Philosophical Society. —G. S. CARTER.   *May*, 1957.

CONTENTS

CHAPTER I

Introduction

IN 1858 the papers by Darwin and Wallace, in which the theory of evolution as directed by natural selection was first set out, were read before the Linnean Society, and in 1859 Darwin published *The Origin of Species*. So, a hundred years ago, the theory in which biologists still believe, modified though it has been, was founded.

The object of this book is to review the development of the theory during the century that has passed since 1858 and 1859. The present is for other reasons besides the centenary an unusually suitable occasion for a re-discussion. The acrimonious disputes of the nineteenth century have died down; and, though the truth of evolution may not even yet be universally admitted, bias on both sides is much less. In biology, work throughout the century has led to continuous modification of the theory, and the consensus of opinion for and against it has fluctuated from time to time. But, in the last thirty years, the progress of biology in all its branches has led to synthesis of a form of the theory which, incomplete as it certainly still is, is in accord with all the known facts, and has come to be very generally accepted by biologists. The present position contrasts with that of forty years ago. Then difficulties in bringing the results of the recent work on Mendelian genetics into agreement with the demands of Darwin's theory led many biologists to doubt whether there was much real truth in the theory. We now have what is apparently a sound and well established theory, and the present, being also the centenary of its publication, seems a suitable occasion to review its development.

For all biologists, whatever the branch of biology they are interested in, knowledge of the evolution of living organisms and its causes is fundamental to their work. The zoologist or botanist who is studying living animals or plants is faced with the fact that evolution is still going on among them, though the changes he is able to observe must be small. He needs to understand how their populations change with time, and he also needs knowledge of the past course of evolution so that he may know how they have come to possess the characters he finds them to have. Those working on historical biology, trying to describe and explain the course of change in the organisms of past ages, and those working on the systematic classification of organisms, need knowledge of the theory of evolution still more evidently, for it alone offers them some hope of reducing their observations to logical order.

Even though all biologists should be interested in evolution and its theory, it does not necessarily follow that they need to study the history of the subject. There may be little doubt that scientific history should have a place in the education of the scientist and is there of value in broadening the student's outlook, but this is not to say that the working scientist will necessarily profit greatly from his knowledge of history in his efforts to advance his subject. To many scientists it seems doubtful that he will. Certainly, the scientist needs to know the logical background of his knowledge, but many doubt whether a study of the steps by which that knowledge was reached in the history of the subject is the best way of getting to know the background. Since this book is concerned with scientific history, some discussion at the outset of its value to scientists and others seems worth-while.

The reasons why scientists doubt the value to them of scientific history seem to be these. Science is not a historical study. Rather it is a logical synthesis; its mode of thought resembles much more closely that of the mathematician than the historian. The scientist is not necessarily interested in the steps by which our present knowledge was reached, for these are often by no means the same as those required by the logic of the subject; and he is usually not at all interested in the mistaken views of former scientists, which, as well as their successes, will have their places in a history of the subject. Chemists today will not find a knowledge of the history of the eighteenth-century belief in phlogiston of any help in planning their work, nor will the astronomer be helped by knowledge of the ptolemaic theory.

These objections assume that scientific history is written as a straight-forward account of the knowledge and theories that have been held from time to time, and nothing more, as a history that is concerned only with the progress of ideas. But even if the history is of that kind, there is more to be said of its value to the scientist. Knowledge of past science may often be used as a textbook of scientific method; the mistakes of past generations may warn us of the types of erroneous deduction that lead to false conclusions. And a study of scientific history may lead us to question our unconscious assumptions, which are often of historical origin. In these indirect ways a scientific history, even if it is entirely impersonal, may be of value to the working scientist.

However, it is not necessary to treat scientific history in this impersonal manner, and a history that considers the personalities of the scientists of the past and their relations with the world outside science may undoubtedly be of value to scientists as well as to others. Study of the lives of those who have advanced science will show how their thought developed both as the result of their own work and by contact with others; and consideration of the advance of science in relation to the intellectual atmosphere of the non-scientific world around it may give a clearer idea of the place of science in the thought of the world at large. This last is perhaps the most important way in which knowledge of scientific history may help the scientist. For science does not advance *in vacuo*. The background of thought in the world outside science influences the scientist's mind and determines his interests, which again influence the directions in which he tries to make advances. (We may go so far as this without accepting the Marxist doctrine that the advances of science are entirely directed towards economic ends.) Further the general atmosphere of thought, both within and outside science, to a large extent determines the recognition that is given to scientific work. The scientist has not finished with his work when it is published. He has then to persuade the world to accept it, and that does not wholly depend on the scientific value of the work; as we shall see Huxley and Haeckel were almost as important as Darwin in forcing acceptance of evolutionary ideas in the nineteenth century. The efficiency of the presentation and the scientist's reputation for reliability and accuracy influence his success in getting his work accepted, but so also does the ease with which the results fit in with the preconceptions of those that read them. Some results being in accord with the intellectual atmosphere of the time will be at once accepted; others, equally sound and important—and perhaps even more novel—may be disregarded because they do not so fit in. This is one reason why scientific work of importance is so often neglected at the time of its publication and only later recognized as valuable.

It is, then, clear that the interactions between scientific thought and the intellectual world outside science are important for the scientist even if we consider only the progress of his work in his subject. It is equally certain that they are important for the rest of the world whenever scientific results have implications outside science. Study of scientific history, if it is treated as dealing with the place of science in the world at large as well as with progress within science, will be concerned with these interactions and will be valuable to both the scientist and the layman.

The history of the theory of evolution within the last century gives many examples of these interactions and they have largely influenced its progress. This book is an attempt to summarize the history from this point of view. There can hardly be a more suitable subject for such treatment, for, during the nineteenth century at least, no scientific subject excited so much interest in the world at large as biological evolution. There are other subjects in science that would almost equally repay discussion of this kind. One is the revolution in the ideas of physics and astronomy during the sixteenth and seventeenth centuries, but the discussion would be more difficult. We are closer to the nineteenth century disputes about evolution and can understand them more easily.

The first part of the book deals with the history up to the end of the nineteenth century. It is not possible to understand the effects produced by the publication of Darwin's work without some consideration of the discussions of evolution that had gone on in the preceding years, for these discussions gave the background on which Darwin wrote. The first two chapters are concerned with this background, and the rest of the first part deals with Darwin's theory and the reactions during the second half of the century to its publication. By the end of the century it had come to be very generally accepted among biologists almost in the form in which Darwin enunciated it.

The second part of the book deals with the present century, and the development of the theory of evolution during that time.

The concept of evolution derives from the truth that the whole world of nature is not in a state of equilibrium but is continually changing, and that the course of its change is directional—not haphazard but moving in a definite direction, towards conditions different from those at earlier stages. That there is continual change in nature on the small scale of our observations is immediately obvious to any observer, and its extension to the whole field of nature is easy. Its truth was in fact recognized very early by the Greek philosophers—Heraclitus, for instance, held that all nature was in a state of flux— and the conclusion that the change is in general directional is accepted. Since the time of the Greeks the concept of evolution has always played a part in the development of scientific thought, though it may have been more consciously recognized in some periods than in others (p. 29).

The concept is, then, general to our appreciation of the natural world; it has a place in the physical sciences as well as in the biological. It does not necessarily imply progress from the simpler to the more complex. In cosmology, for instance, we are often told that the course of evolution is towards uniformity, towards a final state in which the universe is undifferentiated in its parts, and therefore simpler than at present. It is the peculiarity of biological evolution that it has in fact been characterized, in general and apart from many exceptions, by progress from smaller and simpler organisms to larger and more complex. It is this progressive character of biological evolution that any theory of it has primarily to interpret.

We are concerned only with biological evolution, and need not further consider evolution in the physical world. Even in biology we shall be concerned only with that part of evolution for which we have direct and concrete evidence, that is with evolution among the organisms alive today or to be found as fossils. Evolutionary ideas in biology originated with the question whether each type of animal and plant had been separately created or whether they had been evolved from forms unlike themselves—with the problem of the origin of species. This problem was the subject of most of the earlier disputes that we have to discuss, and it was the subject of Darwin's book. But if one species evolves from another, and if this has been going on throughout the history of living organisms, it is clear that all the forms of life may probably be related by the evolutionary process, and we should be able to trace the course of evolution from the simplest organisms to the most complex. Thus, evolution came to be thought of as determining the whole history of the known forms of life in the natural world. From this, extension of the discussion to the question whether evolution also took place at stages earlier in the history of life than those for which we have evidence, so that the simplest organisms we know were evolved from others still simpler, was

B

natural and soon made. A final step was taken when it was asked whether living organisms were evolved at a still earlier stage from non-living matter.

The problem of the origin of the first living organism, that is to say, of a living being capable, as an individual or a race, of indefinitely continued life in a natural, and therefore a changing, environment, has been much discussed, but I want to exclude it from our discussions. It seems to me that we cannot at present reach any worthwhile conclusions on this subject. It may be possible to suggest conditions in which highly complex chemical substances could be formed and would grow, but no suggestions have been made how many of the features needed for the continued life of living organisms could be evolved. One such is the peculiar type of pattern that characterizes the arrangement of the parts in the body of the organism, a type of pattern unlike, as it seems to me, any in non-living nature including that of the crystal. It is much more difficult to see how such characters could be evolved than to imagine the formation of a growing chemical substance, and until we have some ideas concerning their evolution, we cannot discuss to any purpose the evolution of the first organisms. They *may* have evolved from non-living matter, and, if we are to believe that the universe has evolved from the start without outside interference, we must believe that they did, but this is not to say that we can at present profitably discuss their evolution.

I wish further to restrict our discussions. I shall discuss only the evolution of organisms alive today or found as fossils. To so restrict our discussions means that we put aside all the steps of evolution that lay behind the simplest living organisms, for these are simpler than any known fossils. Apart from the bacteria which stand apart with unknown relationships to the rest of the living world, these simplest organisms are the unicellular flagellates. To put aside all evolution behind them is a large restriction, for these free-living cells possess all the characters of the organism that make continued life possible and in many details of their pattern and physiology they show extraordinarily close similarities to more complex organisms. They have, in fact, all the governing patents of life, and it may reasonably be said that all later evolution is no more than elaboration of the general plan laid down at a date before the beginning of our evidence. This is true, but it is perhaps less disturbing than it seems at first sight. So far as we can see, biological evolution has been of the same general nature throughout its course from the first organism onwards; there is no reason to think that the evolutionary process has been essentially different in its earlier and later stages. If we can understand the later steps in evolution, even though these may be only a small part of the whole, our knowledge may reasonably be extrapolated to cover the evolution of the organism at all its stages. Only the origin of the earliest organism from non-living matter seems, so far as our present knowledge goes, to be outside this course of gradual and continuous change and probably to require different principles for its interpretation.

At the other end of the story of evolution there is the origin of man from his animal ancestors. Man's body evolved according to the principles that have controlled evolution in all animals; its evolution needs no special discussion. But since he became self-conscious, those principles have become less and less operative and his evolution has been controlled more and more by tradition. It needs its own discussion on lines very different from those developed in this book. I shall not discuss it. It has often been discussed. Cf. Huxley[1].

However large these limitations of our subject may be, it is clear that what is needed in biology today is an understanding of how and why evolution has proceeded between the simple flagellates and the highest animals and plants. That is what we need to understand life as it is lived today and has been lived in the past of fossiliferous times. It is also the subject of the discussions of the last hundred years.

[1] E.g., in *Evolution in Action*, Chatto and Windus, 1953.

PART I

The Nineteenth Century

CHAPTER 2

The Background to Darwin: the Position in Scientific and General Thought

IN 1859, when *The Origin of Species* was published, Darwin was fifty years old. He had lived through most of the first half of the century, and had been bred up in the biological atmosphere of that period. The possibility that evolution occurs in animals and plants was present to the minds of biologists throughout his lifetime, and several biologists had, as we shall see, discussed it. But at the time he wrote, the reality of evolution was still regarded as no more than a possibility, and no theory in explanation of it had gained at all general acceptance. In considering the background on which Darwin thought and wrote, we may first discuss the reasons why the idea of evolution had arisen among biologists. We can then go on to discuss any theories in explanation of evolution that had been put forward and the causes of their failure to gain general acceptance.

There are many features in the living world that *suggest* the possibility of evolution to any biologist; almost every biological study, however special its aim may be, gives results which are suggestive of evolution. Even if we had no theory of evolution, it would be hard for a biologist to observe living nature and read the work of other biologists without feeling that the idea that each species is a special creation, the only alternative to a belief in evolution, fails to fit the facts. Let us take in order some of these characters of the living world that suggest the possible truth of evolution, and see how far the biological work of the years before Darwin wrote was suggestive of its truth.

1. There is first the fact that animals and plants can be arranged in large groups within each of which the structure shows similarities in all the species. Recognition of these groups dates back to Aristotle who arranged the organisms he knew in a small number of large *phyla*, many of which are the same as the groups we recognize today. Among animals, he distinguished first a group of phyla, the Sanguinea—our Vertebrates—from the Exsanguinea, the invertebrate phyla. Among the vertebrates man, viviparous quadrupeds (mammals), oviparous quadrupeds (reptiles and amphibians), birds, and fishes were placed in separate phyla; the Cetacea (whales and porpoises), which we now recognize as mammals, were given an independent phylum. Today, we include all vertebrates, and some other animals, in a single phylum, the Chordata, but we still recognize all of his sanguineous phyla as groups within the Chordata. Among the invertebrates, Aristotle's phyla of annulose animals (insects and worms), Malacostraca (Crustacea), and Testacea (molluscs, echinoderms—sea-urchins and starfishes) do not agree so closely with our classification, for we separate the insects from the worms uniting insects and Crustacea in the phylum Arthropoda, and placing the worms in another phylum, Annelida. Also, we give separate phyla to the molluscs and echinoderms. The Cephalopoda (octopuses and squids) to which Aristotle gave a separate phylum are now placed in the Mollusca. Nevertheless, it is true that his classification agrees in its broad outlines with ours, and the fact that biologists have been in this general agreement over so wide a stretch of time implies that the classification into

phyla is founded on natural fact and has not arisen in the mind of the biologist.

Aristotle believed that all the animals included in any one of his phyla were built on the same fundamental plan. They differed in the forms of the parts and in 'excess or defect' of parts, but not in the fundamental plan of the body. Here again the modern biologist agrees.

This arrangement of organisms in groups of similar structure—not merely the phyla but also a whole hierarchy of smaller groups within each phylum—was fundamental to the zoology of the seventeenth and eighteenth centuries, when zoologists were concerned mainly with describing animals and classifying them on a system of this kind derived directly from Aristotle. This, in fact, is the basis of Linnaeus' classification.

That organisms can be so classified does not necessarily imply evolution. Neither Aristotle nor Linnaeus had any conception of evolution. Linnaeus indeed, in agreement with the religious thought of his time, regarded each species as a special creation. But it is certainly true that the fact that organisms can be so classified fits in very well with the idea of evolution when that idea comes to be considered. If species are separately created, there is no reason why they should be created in large groups of fundamentally similar structure. If evolution has occurred, similarity of structure necessarily results from evolutionary relationship, and each phylum should be regarded as descended from a single ancestral stock.

2. If a common plan can be found in each of these large groups of organisms, it is natural to ask whether such a plan cannot be found in *all* organisms, whether they cannot all be arranged in a single system. Attempts to do this were very early made; the conception of a *Scala Naturae*, a system of this kind in which the basis

of the arrangement was nothing more than complexity of organization within the organism, dates back to the Greeks. It was commonly present in the minds of eighteenth-century biologists and was stated in what was probably its most extreme form by the Frenchman, Bonnet (1720–93) who called it his *Échelle des Êtres*, on which all organisms, living and not living, were placed. It extended from the simple organization of rocks and minerals to the complexity of man.

Again, there were no evolutionary implications in the conception but, however unsound the plan of a single graded scale was later shown to be—we now know that the relationships of organisms are not along a single line but complexly branching—it did at least emphasize the conception that all organisms can be regarded as parts of a single system and, in so far, may be said to have paved the way for ideas of evolution when these arose.

3. A very active school of zoology at the beginning of the nineteenth century and thoughout most of the first half of that century, indeed the dominant school at that time, was the German abstract or transcendental zoology, usually called Natur-philosophie. This school owed its origin to Goethe more than to any other bio-logist. To it belonged in the nineteenth century many of the leading German biologists (e.g. Serres, Meckel, Oken, etc). It was also influential in other countries. The view of zoology held by this school was related to the conceptions behind the Échelle des Êtres, and in-deed largely derived from them. These zoologists sought to develop the *Scala Naturae* based on complexity of organization into a similar scale founded on a common detailed plan of organization in all organisms. For them, the structure of every organism was merely a modifica-

tion of the single plan common to all. They hoped to build up a system of morphology as one can build up a system of crystal form in crystallography. They extended the idea of parallelism of structure not only to all the organisms of all the phyla but also to repeated parts within the body of a single organism—the vertebrate skull was to them a series of three or four modified vertebrae. The universal plan was common to all organisms, but within each phylum all the species could be regarded as modifications of a more detailed archetype of the phylum, all these archetypes being related. Their comparisons were often very far-fetched and indeed fantastic. The structure of a segment of the insect body was thought to show the same structural elements as a segment of a vertebrate; the placenta was homologized with the gills of fishes and even of molluscs and worms; and the amnion of a vertebrate embryo with the bladder of the cysticercus of a tapeworm.

However fantastic these ideas may seem to us, it is important to realize that they were prevalent, and in Germany dominant, in zoology at a time shortly before that in which Darwin did his work on evolution. It was in these ideas, not always in their most extreme forms, that the minds of many of the elder zoologists of the latter part of the century were formed.

All the work of the eighteenth and early nineteenth centuries that we have so far considered was entirely morphological. The aim was to find a plan behind the great diversity of living forms. Often the plan was regarded as the plan of creation, the plan according to which animals and plants had in the first instance been created, but that interpretation was not necessary to the work. For some the aim was nothing more than to find the order that lay behind natural diversity.

Throughout the history of zoology this has been one of the aims of zoologists. It persisted long after the period of natur-philosophie and is indeed the aim of phylogenetic morphology today, though now the plan sought for is that of evolutionary relationship. It is also the fundamental aim of systematics. A quite different aim, that of understanding how the life of animals is controlled and carried on both within the body and in relation to the environment outside it, has equally been present at all stages of the history of zoology, though it was less prevalent in the eighteenth and early nineteenth centuries than the morphological aim. This is the aim of natural history, physiology and similar studies. Each of these two aims has been dominant from time to time; neither has at any time been completely neglected. We shall find examples of the interplay between them in the more recent history of zoology.

One idea that originated at this time deserves mention, for it played a large part in post-Darwinian discussion. This was the observation that within a phylum the organisms show greater similarities in the early stages of their life-history than in the later stages—the tadpole is more like a fish than a frog is, and the very young stages of all vertebrates are so alike that they cannot be distinguished without some knowledge of morphology. This is undoubtedly true observation. It was emphasized by von Baer (1828) on the basis of a large amount of embryological work.

von Baer's origin was in the transcendental school of natur-philosophie, as is shown by his interpretation of the reason for the greater resemblances of young stages. He believed that these stages are more alike because they are closer to the archetype of the group to which they belong; he held that differentiation within a phylum results mainly from different development during the later stages of the life-history.

In general, the transcendental school of biology resembled the biologists of the eighteenth century in that their conceptions had no evolutionary background. These biologists aimed only at comparing structure and at building up an abstract theory of organismal form from the comparisons. Their outlook was also very often vitalistic—in the true sense of vitalism, that in living organisms there is a vital principle not comparable to anything in non-living nature. This was largely responsible for the antagonism of many of the German biologists to Darwin's theory when it was published (cf. p. 73ff). Nevertheless, in emphasizing parallelism in the structure of organisms the work of the natur-philosophers did suggest the possibility of evolution and pave the way for the later development of evolutionary ideas.

Equally, there was no necessary evolutionary background to von Baer's work. It could find its place in natur-philosophie as a further means by which the structure of the archetype could be determined. But, when the concept of evolution is considered, the greater resemblances of young stages do suggest that the relatedness of organisms to each other is closer than appears from study of the adult forms. von Baer's work was therefore in favour of an evolutionary interpretation of the resemblances, and he himself admitted a certain amount of evolution between closely similar organisms. He was one of the comparatively few biologists of his time to do so. He did not believe in a general theory of evolution applied to the whole living world.

4. We have so far considered only the morphological studies in biology that were carried out in the period

before Darwin wrote, but it must not be forgotten that all branches of biology were rapidly advancing throughout the eighteenth and early nineteenth centuries. This is true in spite of the fact that by far the greater volume of work at that time was given either to morphological studies such as those of the natur-philosophers or to the systematics of animals, the recording and description of animals and placing them in their correct systematic categories. Systematics was indeed even more than morphology the interest of the biologists of the time, especially in the eighteenth century before natur-philosophie became fashionable. In the eighteenth century the greatest names in biology were Linnaeus and Buffon, both descriptive systematists. In the nineteenth century we have among many others Cuvier, a systematist and student of animal structure, and Lamarck, also essentially a systematist.

Systematics and morphology suggest the possibility of evolution in the ways that have been discussed. But so did all the other branches of biology. Animals and plants were being collected from many parts of the world and in the process of collecting them much knowledge of their natural history and distribution was being gained. Physiologists were studying the working of the body of the organism and its parts.

Each of these branches of biology yields facts that suggest the possibility of evolution, and must have done so to the biologists who observed them. The facts of distribution and natural history provided much of the evidence that Darwin elaborated in 'The Origin', and the physiologist cannot help being impressed by the fact that in general organisms agree in their physiology in proportion to their closeness in the systematic classification. There is a systematics of physiology as well as of structure and, broadly at any rate, the two are in agreement. If the results of the structural systematists suggest evolution, so also do those of the physiologists.

5. One of the most important influences on the biological thought of the first half of the nineteenth century was the publication of Lyell's *Principles of Geology* in 1830. It certainly very largely influenced Darwin.

That fossils are in truth records of the animals and plants of the past was recognized in the eighteenth century, and in 1785 Hutton published his *Theory of the Earth*, in which he held that the earth had continued for long periods under conditions not essentially unlike the present and that the sedimentary strata are the results of deposition of the breakdown products of earlier rocks during this long life of the earth.

This 'Uniformitarian' theory met much opposition at the time it was published. In the years before its publication, most geologists had found it necessary to postulate a sequence of periods in which the rocks were laid down by precipitation from a world-wide ocean. Between these periods the waters retreated and the continents appeared. This was known as the Neptunist theory. Since it was necessary to Hutton's theory that the world has existed as we know it for a very long time, it came up against the biblical story of creation much more directly than the older theory, for most of the supporters of that theory accepted a creation 6,000 years ago and Noah's flood also fitted well into their theory as one of the periodic disturbances of the history of the world. The Uniformitarian theory therefore met religious as well as scientific opposition.

Later (1820–30) the Neptunist theory was developed into what became known as the Catastrophic theory. By that time it had become clear that the age of the world was more than 6,000 years and the days of Genesis were interpreted as periods of indefinite length. According to the catastrophists, they were separated by catastrophes, in which animal and plant life was destroyed, to be recreated at the beginning of the next epoch. The Flood was the last of these catastrophes.[1]

Acceptance of the Uniformitarian theory was by no means general when Lyell published his book in 1830. Indeed, Huxley writing in 1880[2] says that the catastrophic theory was in 1830 still the dominant view.

By collecting an immense amount of evidence in favour of the uniformitarian theory Lyell convinced the scientific world in general of its truth, and therefore of the fact that the past history of the world—and of life upon it—could be read in the sedimentary rocks. He also showed that the igneous rocks needed no world-wide catastrophes to explain their present forms. But even in 1858, belief in the catastrophic theory was by no means extinct.

Lyell did not believe in evolution when he wrote his book. But the result of his book was to establish a picture of the history of the world which gave a possible background in geology for evolution if on other grounds it was shown to have occurred. Indeed, more than this can be said. If the living world was not destroyed by a catastrophe at the end of each epoch, it must have given rise to the life of the next epoch which could be shown by study of the fossils to be different. Change of form, and therefore evolution, must have taken place. Huxley remarks that 'Darwin is the natural successor of Hutton and Lyell, and *The Origin of Species* the logical sequence of *The Principles of Geology*'. Neither Lyell nor most of

[1] C. C. Gillispie, *Genesis and Geology*, Harvard Univ. Press, 1951.
[2] *The Coming of Age of The Origin of Species*, 1880.

the contemporary biologists at that time drew these conclusions, though Lyell later became convinced of the truth of evolution. Still, his book very clearly prepared the way for belief in evolution.

6. For us the important conclusion to be drawn from the whole of this discussion is that any study of animals and plants, and especially study of their structure, must as it proceeds continually emphasize their similarities and suggest that these similarities may be put down to relatedness. All such study must therefore make easier acceptance of belief in evolution when it is proposed. This was certainly true of many lines of work in the eighteenth and early nineteenth centuries.

So far nothing has been said of thought outside science in the earlier part of the nineteenth century. There is no doubt that much of the general atmosphere of thought was powerfully opposed to any evolutionary theory throughout that time. Partly this derived from the unavoidable conflict between belief in evolution and the doctrines then held by very many to be essential to religion and partly to the metaphysical implications that seemed to be implied by a belief in evolution. Ever since the publication of Hutton's book in 1785, the discord between the conclusions of the scientists and the story of Genesis had been openly discussed. As the years passed the progress of scientific work had modified the position taken up by both sides. By 1850, some of the better-informed writers on the side of religion had come to realize that it was impossible to maintain a literal belief in the story of the Flood, and certainly in Archbishop Usher's data for the creation of the world, 6,000 years ago. This development was especially clear after the publication of Lyell's book. But it seems that

c

these discussions largely passed over the heads of the general Christian populace. Fundamentalist beliefs were still very generally held, and the revival of religion towards the middle of the century was predominantly fundamentalist. We will discuss the religious opposition to Darwin's views in more detail later (Ch. 5). Here something may be said of the philosophical implications, which had many religious implications.

The success of scientific method in the physical sciences in the earlier part of the century had been great, and the material progress that followed the industrial revolution had resulted from application of this new knowledge to industry. The successes of science were leading, at least among the physical scientists, to the belief that the scientific method could be applied to all subjects of thought, and that it was indeed the only successful method. This, if accepted, implied philosophical materialism, for science is applicable only in the material sphere. That outlook was spreading among the scientists, but many of the academic philosophers were still following the great analytical metaphysicians of the eighteenth century such as Kant and Hegel (e.g. Sir Wm. Hamilton in Britain and most of the Germans). To those who thought along their lines, complete materialism was not a possible creed. It resulted that the thought of the scientists became divorced from that of the philosophers. Thus Sir William Dampier says in his *History of Science*:[1]

'For about half a century, especially in Germany, this separation between science and philosophy persisted. The Hegelians despised the experimenters, somewhat as did the Greek philosophers. The men of science disliked and finally ignored the Hegelians. Even Helm-

[1] p. 314, 3rd Edition, 1942.

holtz, in deploring this attitude . . . limited philosophy to its critical function—the elucidation of the theory of knowledge—and denied its claim to attack other more speculative problems, such as the deeper questions of the nature of reality and the meaning of the Universe'. The philosophers could not accept materialism, and evolution seemed to extend analysis of the scientific kind in the living world and perhaps even to man. They naturally opposed it.

Another line of thought antagonistic to a belief in evolution was that developed in Paley's *Evidences of Christianity*. The argument from design as there set out—the argument that the parts of organisms show evidence of having been designed for the uses to which they are put in the lives of the organisms—was undoubtedly influential. It seemed necessarily to imply that these features could not have been derived from the unthinking action of the forces of nature, and therefore that a theory of evolution that relied on the action of these forces for its results and allowed no other influences was unreasonable.

Nevertheless, even the general atmosphere of thought of the time was, when Darwin wrote, becoming more favourable to discussion of the problems of evolution. Materialism was becoming a wide-spread belief among scientists—or at least among the physical scientists, for the biologists did not by any means so generally accept it. Reality was thought of as composed of fives-ball atoms influenced only by the physical forces and conditions of gravity, heat, electricity and so on. Science was the system by which we gained knowledge of this real external world—not as we may now think an analysis and synthesis of our experience. This materialistic outlook originated from the results of the physical sciences. It was an entirely sound background for them at the time and for their progress. It has indeed served successfully up to the present century, when many think it has broken down in face of the recent advances in physical science.

Before the middle of the century, the success of the chemists in synthesizing some compounds previously known only from living bodies, and of the physiologists in showing that physical laws can be applied to many of the activities of organisms, suggested that the same materialistic system could be extended to the phenomena of biology. Not merely physiological activities but behaviour, habit and the whole realm of psychology were then assumed to be equally open to the same type of investigation as the phenomena of physics, and it was therefore concluded that they were of the same materialistic nature. From this it was an easy step to the claim that the scientific method is the only means of acquiring knowledge, that there is no real knowledge outside science, a view that has been held by many in more recent times (Haeckel, Hogben).

The impulse behind this desire of the scientists for a purely materialistic conception of the nature of all knowledge was undoubtedly their justifiable feeling that they must be allowed to extend the domain of science as far as their methods could be shown to apply. This led them, illogically as we may now think, to deny any other source of knowledge, philosophical or religious. Dingle in discussing the scientific outlook in 1851[1] says:

'What was disputed was the relative weight of different kinds of evidence concerning what has happened—on the one hand rational inference from existing events; on

[1] *Brit. J. Philos Sci.*, **2**, 85, 1951.

the other the authority of the Scriptures. What the scientists were unconsciously fighting for was freedom for their scientific process of finding relations between experiences; and what the religionists were unconsciously fighting for was the validity of their spiritual experience.'

By no means all scientists were complete materialists. Many (e.g. Whewell, Herschel, Buckland) were staunch upholders of the Church and did their utmost to limit disagreement between science and religion. Others who were less sympathetic to religion (e.g. Huxley) qualified their materialism by admitting the necessity for a Creator, Designer or First Great Cause. Lay opinion, which could not always recognize the religious and philosophical implications of materialism, was coming to regard it less unfavourably. To many it seemed that the extension of science to new fields was natural and inevitable, and the development of a theory of evolution was clearly such an extension. Science, both its method and its philosophy, was becoming fashionable.

The spread of materialistic ideas was helped by the growth of a new school of philosophic and political thought, that of the Utilitarians and other rationalists. This school became influential in the thirty years before 1858, and its influence was crystallized by the publication of J. S. Mill's *System of Logic* in 1843. The thought of these schools was empirical. Mill's outlook is summarized by M. H. Carré[1] in the following sentences:

'The ultimate premises of knowledge are our own bodily sensations and mental feelings. The facts known *per se* are "anyone's present sensations, or other states of subjective consciousness." We are not aware of objects directly but of the sensations we receive from

[1] M. H. Carré *Phases of Thought in England*, p. 314.

these objects; the objects are not perceived but are believed to exist. All of which we are aware is a thread of sensations, thoughts, emotions and volitions; of the nature of the body and the mind further than the sensations we do not know anything. . . . "Man" simply means the whole of the attributes connoted by the word; the supposed essences of things are names arbitrarily attached to certain attributes.' Such an outlook was far from complete materialism but it was undoubtedly far more favourable to scientific discussion of the nature of the living world and the question of its evolution than was that of the German metaphysicians.

So we see that in these various ways, both in biology and in the outlook of those who were not biologists, thought was moving in directions favourable to consideration of the problems of evolution. The time was becoming ripe for acceptance of a belief in evolution if a basis of fact and deduction sound enough to convince biological opinion could be provided. Before this time many biologists had considered the possibility of the truth of evolution. Some had expressed belief in it and one theory to account for it, that of Lamarck, had been put forward. We must now discuss the history of these pre-Darwinian discussions of evolution and the state of biological opinion on the subject in 1858.

CHAPTER 3

The Background to Darwin: Development of Ideas Concerning Evolution

WE need not go far back in considering the development of evolutionary ideas. Some of the Greek philosophers believed that the forms of animals and plants are not constant, and they may therefore be credited with the basic idea of evolution. Empedocles, for instance, is said to have held that animal forms are in time replaced by more perfect forms. But these ideas were not, so far as we know, developed by them and did not greatly influence modern thought on the problems of evolution. Aristotle, by far the greatest biologist of classical times, does not discuss evolution.

We need not even discuss whether the biologists of the Renaissance had any ideas concerning evolution. Professor Butterfield in his book on *The Origins of Science*[1] points out that the atmosphere of the Renaissance was not favourable to the development of evolutionary ideas. Men were then absorbing the new knowledge of classical times and looking at those times across the dark ages of the mediaeval centuries. They were concerned with a return to the classical standard, and a progress in the world with time—a continuous evolution in man or nature—did not come naturally to them. It was only at the end of the seventeenth century that evolutionary ideas appeared at all commonly. They developed slowly throughout the eighteenth century.

[1] Ch. 12, pp. 191 ff.

In the eighteenth century the idea of Progress in human affairs and in nature was current (e.g. Helvetius, Condorcet), but in general such ideas carried no implications of the biological evolution of one form from another, and references to evolution in the natural world are usually casual and incidental. Sir William Dampier in his *History of Science*[1] makes the point that until towards the end of the eighteenth century evolutionary ideas are to be found much more in the writings of the philosophers than of the biologists. He quotes Bacon, Descartes, Leibnitz, Kant and at the end of the eighteenth century Goethe, though he was also a biologist.

Dampier points out that this was natural, for the biological evidence was not then sufficient to form the basis of a theory of evolution, and the subject was therefore not ripe for scientific discussion, whereas the philosopher in building up his logical view of the world was free to discuss this, as every other, subject. He also points out that the philosophic discussion served a useful purpose in keeping the subject before the biologists' minds until it could be discussed scientifically.

This being so, we cannot expect any large discussion of evolution by eighteenth-century biologists. The subject is mentioned by many but usually only as an aside; it was not a subject in which they were greatly interested. It was also a dangerous subject, for even in the eighteenth century the power of the Church was considerable in many countries, and not to be lightly opposed. Buffon, for instance, in the course of his structural consideration of animals, finds it necessary to mention the possibility that one species may be derived from another, though he finds great difficulties

[1] pp. 292-3, 3rd edition, 1942.

in that view. He also says of quadrupeds that they may perhaps be reduced to a few families from which all the rest may be derived. After a supposition that all the species in these families may be derived from one, he adds the doubtfully sincere sentence—'But no, it is certain, by revelation, that all animals have equally enjoyed the grace of creation'. He was forced in 1751 by the Sorbonne to recant on the possibility of the derivation of one species from another.

Buffon has other passages that show that he realized at least that the forms of organisms change with time.[1] He was writing in pre-revolution France, and it is possible that if he had lived in a protestant country he might have been more explicit in his discussion of evolutionary ideas. But the Swede Linnaeus, who shares with him the reputation of the greatest eighteenth-century biologist, never allowed the possibility of evolutionary change between species. If these two could go no farther, it is not surprising that lesser men did not. It will not be worth our while to recount all the references to evolution by biologists in the eighteenth century.

There was, however, one biologist at the end of the century who stated much more definitely his belief in the possibility, and indeed the probability, of evolution. This was Erasmus Darwin, the grandfather of Charles Darwin. His conclusions were set out in his *Zoonomia* (1794). They can best be given in quotations:

'When we revolve in our minds the metamorphoses of animals, as from the tadpole to the frog; secondly, the changes produced by artificial cultivation, as in the breeds of horses, dogs and sheep; thirdly, the changes produced by conditions of climate and season, as in the

---

[1] Cf. Butterfield, *Origins of Modern Science*, pp. 203–5.

sheep of warm climates being covered with hair instead of wool, and the hares and partridges of colder climates becoming white in winter; when further we observe the changes produced by habit, as seen especially in men of different occupations; or the changes produced by artificial mutilations and prenatal influences, as in the crossing of species and production of monsters; fourthly, when we observe the essential unity of plan in all warm-blooded animals—we are led to believe that they have been alike produced from a single living filament.'

'From thus meditating on the minute portion of time in which many of the above changes have been produced, would it be too bold to imagine, in the great length of time since the earth began to exist, perhaps millions of years before the commencement of the history of mankind, that all warm-blooded animals have arisen from one living filament?'

If we interpret, as we clearly should, 'a single living filament' to mean a single ancestral stock, the position taken up by the grandfather is extraordinarily close to that of the grandson in *The Origin of Species*. We have here, in fact, a short summary of much of the evidence set out in favour of the truth of evolution in that book. No theory to explain how evolution is brought about is given; E. Darwin did not attempt to give such a theory. He was however the first to set out the evidence for evolution so clearly.

Erasmus Darwin was followed by others in the early part of the nineteenth century who admitted that evidence could be found that seemed to support the possibility of evolution, though few believed it to have taken place. Cuvier, von Baer and some others may have admitted a small amount of evolutionary change, as Buffon came near to doing earlier, and Geoffrey St. Hilaire emphasized that change may occur in an animal under the influence of environmental conditions. None of these believed in the evolution of the living world as a whole.

The most important pre-Darwinian biologist who had a full belief in evolution, and the only biologist before Darwin to propose a theory in explanation of it, was the Frenchman Lamarck. His conclusions were published in his *Hist. Nat. des Animaux sans Vertébres*, 1816. They are stated in the following four 'laws'.

'1. Life, by its own forces, tends continually to increase the volume of every body possessing it, and to extend the dimensions of its parts, up to a limit which it brings about itself.

'2. The production of a new organ in an animal body results from the arisal and continuance of a new need, and from the new movement which this need brings into being and sustains.

'3. The degree of development of organs and their force of action are always proportionate to the use made of these organs.

'4. All that has been acquired, imprinted or changed in the organization of the individual during the course of its life is preserved by generation and transmitted to the new individuals that descend from the individual so modified.'[1]

The first of these laws is a statement of supposed fact. We now know that it is very generally but not universally true. The continual increase of size in evolution is seen not only in the whole range of organisms but also in many restricted groups of terrestrial

[1] Quoted from the translation by E. S. Russell, *Form and Function*, 1916, p. 221.

animals such as the horses and elephants, but there are also groups of animals in which evolution has resulted in decrease of size. We do not attribute these changes of size in evolution to an inherent property of living matter but to the action of selection working on advantages that increased or decreased size gives to the animal (cf. p. 166). In his appeal to life's own 'forces' Lamarck is clearly vitalistic, since it must be presumed that he thought these forces different in nature from those in the non-living.

In the second law Lamarck gives no indication of the means by which the need and movement produces the new organ, but elsewhere he says that in the simpler animals the response is a direct effect of actions due to the need. In more complex animals he ascribed the effect to an unconscious 'sentiment intérieur', again a clearly vitalistic conception.

These two laws thus display a markedly vitalistic outlook. They do not attribute any mechanistic cause to the effects, and therefore do not open the way to any further advance by use of the method of scientific investigation. Probably for this reason, since scientific biology is necessarily mechanistic, they have been almost entirely disregarded by later biologists.

The truth of the third law will be admitted; the increase in the muscles of a blacksmith's arm and the shrivelling of a paralysed limb are well-known and obvious examples of its truth. The use made of an organ, and therefore its degree of development in the individual, are undoubtedly determined by the animal's habits in its life within its environment. But the truth of the third law cannot be used as a principle of evolution except in conjunction with the fourth law. Unless characters 'acquired' during the life-history of an animal are handed on to succeeding generations, they cannot play any part in the evolution of the race. Discussion since Lamarck's time has therefore centred on the question of the inheritance of these 'acquired characters'. Darwin was disposed to accept it as a real, though not important, principle in evolution, but in the last century, in spite of much effort to prove its truth, no incontrovertible evidence in favour of it has been put forward, and it is very difficult to bring its truth into line with our present knowledge of genetics. It is now generally discredited, but, as we shall see (p. 87ff), argument about it played a large part in post-Darwinian discussion, and may be revived in the future (cf. p. 191).

Every attempt to explain evolution must concern itself with the conditions that control the life of animals as well as with their structure, for evolution takes place in the natural life of animals in their environment—it is in fact a phenomenon in natural history. To anyone thinking about evolution the question must arise whether the habits and functions of animals determine their structure, or whether structure determines habits. Lamarck's conclusion was that structure follows habit and function, and he attributed evolutionary change to functional change within the body of animals. In this he differed from Darwin, who, as we shall see, attributed the changes to the conditions present in the environment outside the animal. Nevertheless, he agreed with Darwin in his departure from the morphological outlook that we have previously discussed. As we have seen (pp. 16-17), the morphologists aimed at finding a plan in animal nature hidden behind its diversity. Lamarck and Darwin were not primarily looking for such a plan, but trying to explain the causation of some of the phenomena of the life of animals in nature, namely the evolutionary changes that they undergo.

Lamarck's insistence on function as the driving force of evolution has probably been the reason why his theory has always appealed much more to the physiologists than to the naturalists and other biologists. Since his time there have always been many physiologists who have accepted his views, but the proportion of zoologists and botanists who have done so has been small. Almost all the zoologists and botanists of the early half of the nineteenth century discussed Lamarck's theory and most of them criticized it adversely; Cuvier and Lyell certainly did so. It was unsuccessful in shaping opinion then, as it has been to a very large extent since. It was in the background when Darwin wrote, but it had had very little effect on biological thought except among some of the physiologists.

We may ask why Lamarck's theory was so generally discredited. The reasons seem to have been complex; at least the following considerations were behind them:

1. The vitalism that was so evident in some of his laws was in opposition to the materialism of scientific thought and denied the hope of further advance by investigation on materialistic lines. It is true that some at least of the biologists were vitalists, especially among the Germans, but the materialism of physical science was becoming fashionable and was extending to scientists in other fields.

2. Lyell would have none of it in spite of the fact that its geological background was uniformitarian. His objection was mainly that the evidence was not good enough. Lamarck was always ready to suggest a theory whether the evidence for it was there or not. He appears

to regard his aim as rather to suggest possible explanations than to show by evidence that they are real in nature, or indeed that the facts they are suggested to explain are real. Lyell did not at that time accept evolution as a real fact of nature and was therefore not attracted to a theory in explanation of it.

3. The main zoological interest at the time was morphological. Natur-philosophie was very influential, and men were interested rather in archetypes than in explaining evolution. Lamarck's ideas were too different from those of most morphologists to be readily accepted by them.

4. Cuvier, whose weight of reputation was great, rejected the theory because he saw no sufficient evidence to force him to believe in evolution, and because Lamarck's functional outlook ran up against his mainly morphological standpoint.

5. Evolutionists were regarded as 'wild men'. Traditional opinion, biological as well as religious, was on the whole against them, and men were not prepared for so large a change of outlook unless the evidence could be shown to be irresistible. In addition, belief in evolution was still dangerous. It had against it not only the opposition of the Church but also the anti-materialist views of many intellectual circles, still strong although the dominance of materialism among the scientists was increasing.

Even though Lamarck's theory was not accepted by many biologists, the value of his contribution to the discussion of evolutionary problems was great. His support of uniformitarianism was valuable, and by putting forward the first theory to explain the causes of evolution, he at least made biologists realize that the traditional disbelief was not unquestionably right. After his time the possibility that evolution was true was always at the back of men's minds.

In the years that followed the publication of Lamarck's book, very many biologists recognized the possibility that evolution occurs in nature, and several—Darwin mentions thirty-four in his introduction to *The Origin of Species*—stated their acceptance of its truth to a greater or less degree. But no great advances were made. The publication of Lyell's *Principles of Geology* was certainly valuable, but its value to the discussion was indirect. He paved the way for Darwin but did not make any advance of his own. He could hardly have done so, since he did not himself believe in evolution at that time.

Some books were published in which evolution was discussed. One in which evolutionary ideas were clearly set out was *The Vestiges of Creation* published anonymously in 1844 but almost certainly by Robert Chambers. It was a popular book with a wide circulation and its value was chiefly that it did much to prepare the public outside biology for Darwin's work. Scientifically, it was by no means a great work; it was indeed weak in that its argument was often loose and woolly, and it added very little to the scientific discussion of the questions. This did not however prevent its having considerable influence on popular opinion. The author says:

'The proposition determined after much consideration is that the series of animated beings from the simplest and oldest to the highest and most recent are, under the providence of God, the results, *first*, of an impulse which has been imparted to the forms of life advancing them in definite times, by generation, through grades of organization terminating in the highest dicotyledons and vertebrata, these grades being few in number and

generally marked by intervals of organic character
which we find to be a practical difficulty in ascertaining
affinities: *second*, of another impulse connected with
the vital forces tending, in the course of generations, to
modify organic structures in accordance with external
circumstances, as food, the nature of the habitat and
meteoric agencies, these being the "adaptations" of the
natural theologian.'

Here belief in evolution is definitely stated, but the
standpoint is not very different from that of Erasmus
Darwin fifty years before. The author's insistence on
adaptation as a cause of change of structure is interesting
as a forecast of the views of Darwin.

Another book which shows the general interest in the
question of evolution, though it cannot be called a
scientific discussion of the subject, may be mentioned
here. This was Philip Gosse's *Omphalos*, published in
1856, three years before *The Origin of Species*. Gosse
was a member of the fundamentalist sect of the Ply-
mouth Brethren, and held a firm belief in the story of
Genesis as given by revelation. He was however impressed by the scientific evidence for evolution, and he
hoped to resolve the contradiction between that evidence
and his religious beliefs by the argument of his book.
He accepted the biblical story of the creation of the
world a few thousand years ago, but he pointed out
that the world when created must have been a going
world and would have appeared to have a past before
creation. Trees would have been full-grown and animals
adult as well as young. The world, in fact, must have
been created with a past and this might have extended
even to fossils in the rocks. It was, he thought, these
appearances of a pre-creational world that the scientists
were studying. The book was not taken seriously—he

D

was unfairly criticized as believing that the fossils were placed in the rocks to deceive the scientist—and to his great disappointment it had little effect on general opinion.

In the early nineteenth century, as in the eighteenth, the question of evolution was discussed by philosophers as well as by biologists. Though most of the philosophers could not accept materialism as a philosophic belief, this did not mean that they would not consider the concept of evolution in the material world of science. Of those that did so one who expressed a full belief in evolution was Herbert Spencer (1852, 1857), a biologist as well as a philosopher. Before the publication of Darwin's book, Spencer very largely accepted Lamarck's theory. In his Autobiography he says:

'Up to that time . . . I held that the sole cause of organic evolution is the inheritance of functionally-produced modifications. *The Origin of Species* made it clear to me that I was wrong, and that the larger part of the facts cannot be due to any such cause.' His earlier conception of evolution was that it resulted from a continually changing harmony or equilibrium in the organism between elements of organization that become integrated into the unity of the organism and at the same time differentiated to give rise to the varying forms of the organisms we find. The cause of the changes in the equilibrium were mainly those set out by Lamarck. He thus does not, from the scientific outlook, advance towards a theory of evolution beyond Lamarck's position, but to us his importance lies in his clear and definite acceptance of evolution as a true fact of nature.

It will be worth while to summarize the position at the time of the publication of *The Origin of Species*. Our discussion has led to the following conclusions:

  1. A uniformitarian theory of the history of the world

was accepted by most informed scientific opinion. This implied that the world had continued more or less in its present condition for a very long time. So far as science was concerned, the complete truth of the story of Genesis was discarded, but this was not true of popular opinion, and fundamentalism was still the predominant theological belief of the general public, not only in England but also on the continent of Europe and in America.

2. Among biologists the idea of evolution had been discussed for many years and some had expressed their belief that a restricted amount of evolution takes place in nature. Very few believed that in the living world as a whole diversity is due to evolution, and the rank and file of biologists did not believe in any evolution, usually on the ground that the evidence in favour of it was insufficient. They did not, apparently, draw the conclusion that in the absence of evolution creation must have taken place whenever a new species appeared, which palaeontology shows to have occurred throughout geological time. More probably they regarded the whole question of the origin of new forms of life as not yet ripe for discussion.

3. Lamarck's theory had not been influential. Few were convinced by his work. It was discarded by most, partly because of the taint of vitalism present in it, partly because he provided little real evidence that the essential evolutionary processes postulated by him were active in nature, and partly because biology was still dominantly morphological and Lamarck's theory, based on changes of function and habit, was too foreign to the prevalent biological thought of the time to be accepted readily by all but a few.

4. Scientific materialism had been gaining ground

since the industrial revolution, and many scientists, especially among the physicists, were coming to regard the scientific method as the only sound means of attaining knowledge. This outlook was less widespread among the biologists, and outside science it was opposed by many philosophers and by the theologians. It was, however, becoming popular in the world at large owing to the great successes of the physical sciences.

5. The general position was that Darwin was lucky in that the time was ripe for the publication of a theory of evolution. The scientific and philosophical background for it was there. But it needed Darwin's elaboration of the evidence and his inauguration of the theory to convince men of the truth of evolution. If he had failed to give either the evidence or the theory, his book might have had no more influence than Lamarck's.

After so much earlier discussion of evolution, and in this favourable atmosphere, it might be thought that in 1858 biologists should have been expecting and hoping for solution of the problems of evolution in the near future, but this was not so. Darwin in his *Autobiography*[1] describes the position just before his work was published, as it seemed to him:

'It has sometimes been said that the success of "*The Origin*" proved . . . that men's minds were prepared for it. I do not think that that is strictly true, for I occasionally sounded not a few naturalists, and never happened to come across a single one who seemed to doubt about the permanence of species. Even Lyell and Hooker, though they would listen with interest to me, never seemed to agree. I tried once or twice to explain to able men what I meant by Natural Selection, but signally failed. What I believe was strictly true is that

---

[1] *Life and Letters of C. Darwin*, vol. I, p. 87.

innumerable well-observed facts were stored in the minds of naturalists ready to take their proper places as soon as any theory that would receive them was sufficiently explained.'

If we leave aside the minority that believed in evolution, it would probably be true to say that men were more or less subconsciously thinking of the subject but had not got farther than that. Some may have gone further; Huxley, for instance, describes[1] his state of mind at the time as one of 'critical expectancy'. But he also says: ' . . . I imagine that most of those of my contemporaries who thought seriously about the matter were very much in my own state of mind—inclined to say to both Mosaists and Evolutionists, "a plague on both your houses", and disposed to turn aside from an interminable and apparently fruitless discussion, to labour in the fertile fields of ascertainable fact.' The majority were not likely to admit the truth of so revolutionary a theory, one that required so large a change in their whole intellectual outlook, until they were forced to do so by overpowering evidence. This position often recurs in science. A theory that is really new, and requires more than further development of current thought, is often silently disregarded, at least for a time. But a true theory so opposed will build up a pressure of accumulating evidence and will break through the resistance damming it when the evidence becomes sufficient and is clearly stated. We have seen one example of this in the disbelief of the uniformitarian theory in geology before Lyell published his book. Another is the general lack of belief in evolution before Darwin's work was known, and its rapid acceptance after his book was published.

[1] *Idem*, vol. 2, p. 195, 196–7.

CHAPTER 4

Darwin and 'The Origin of Species'

CHARLES DARWIN was born at Shrewsbury in 1809. From 1818 to 1825 he was at Shrewsbury School, then under a famous headmaster, Dr. Butler. He showed little ability in the Classics and left when he was sixteen. His next two years were spent at Edinburgh reading at the University a course in Medicine, but he was not interested in that subject, and in 1828 he went up to Cambridge intending to read for Holy Orders. He spent the years 1828–31 at Cambridge.

In early years at Shrewsbury he had shown interest in natural history, and this interest developed at Edinburgh where he attended lectures on Geology, made biological friends and read two papers on subjects in marine biology to the Plinian Society. At Cambridge his biological interests developed further under the influence of his friend Henslow, who was Professor of Botany. He was not interested in his academic course, though he succeeded in taking his B.A. in 1831. In his reading he seems to have been most impressed by Paley's *Evidences of Christianity* which he admired and by which he was influenced. Most of his time was spent in shooting and studying natural history, especially collecting beetles. He also knew Sedgwick, the Professor of Geology, and studied that subject. He was in fact in these early years laying broadly-based foundations for his later work on geology and natural history. Later he said—'the only evil I found in Cambridge was its being too pleasant.' At that time this may well have been a fair criticism.

In 1831 he was appointed as naturalist on the *Beagle*, which was then setting out for a cruise round the world under Captain Fitzroy. He owed this appointment to Professor Henslow. There is no doubt that it was his experiences during the five years of the voyage that determined his later career. He had gradually given up his intention of becoming a clergyman, and during these five years his delight in scientific observation and investigation increased. In his Autobiography he says[1]:

'Looking backwards I can now perceive how my love for science gradually preponderated over every other taste. During the first two years [of the voyage] my old passion for shooting survived in nearly full force, and I shot myself all the birds and animals for my collection; but gradually I gave up my gun more and more, and finally altogether, to my servant, as shooting interfered with my work, more especially with making out the geological structure of a country. I discovered, though unconsciously and insensibly, that the pleasure of observing and reasoning was a much higher one than that of skill and sport.'

It is to be remembered that until he returned from his voyage, and indeed later, he was as much interested in geology as in natural history.

It was in this voyage that he got his real knowledge of animal life in nature. Afterwards, whatever he was doing, he was at heart a naturalist, interested in observing and explaining the lives of animals as they are lived in their natural environments.

It was also during the voyage that he became convinced of the mutability of animal species. The possibility that evolution occurs in nature must have been known to him before, for, as we have seen in the last

[1] *Life and Letters of C. Darwin*, edtd. F. Darwin, 1887, vol. 1, p. 63.

chapter, it was generally present to the minds of the biologists of that time. But it was his observations during the voyage—the variation in structure among the many different but closely related species of birds on the neighbouring islands of the Galapagos, the changes of structure correlated with changes of climate that he found in South American animals, and many other pieces of evidence—that convinced him that natural species are not permanent, and therefore that evolution is a real fact.

After his return he spent three months at Cambridge and then lived from 1837 to 1842 in London. He married in 1839. In 1842 he moved to Downe in Kent where he lived until his death in 1882.

He started work on the origin of species in 1837, but during the years immediately following his return from his voyage he was also engaged in publishing the results of his work on the *Beagle*. His 'Journal and Remarks' was published as vol. iii of the 'Narrative of the Voyage' in 1839, his book on 'Coral Reefs' in 1842, that on the 'Geology of Volcanic Islands' in 1844, and that on the 'Geology of South America' in 1846. From 1846 he was also working on the morphology and systematics of the barnacles (Cirripedia). He published two monographs on the group, one on the fossil Lepadidae in 1851 and the other on the whole sub-class Cirripedia in two parts in 1851 and 1854. This was Darwin's only morphological and systematic work. It added much to our knowledge of the group—he described, for instance, the minute and parasitic males of some species. He tells us that he felt that morphological work on some group of animals was necessary if he was to be accepted as a serious biologist, but he also says that he doubts if the work was worth the great expenditure of time he gave to it.

In 1839 he read Malthus' work on Population[1] which suggested to him the idea of natural selection and its function in nature of removing the less efficient organisms. From that time he was continually collecting evidence in support of his belief in the mutability of species and of his theory of how it comes about. In 1856, advised by Lyell, he started to write an account of his views on a scale—as he says in his Autobiography—three or four times as extensive as that which was afterwards followed in *The Origin of Species*. But in the summer of 1858 he received a letter from A. R. Wallace, a biologist who was collecting animals in the Malay archipelago, containing an essay in which he expressed views very like, but not identical with, Darwin's own. Wallace had also read Malthus and had immediately come to the idea of natural selection and in other ways to conclusions similar to those that Darwin had been working on for twenty years.

On receipt of this letter Darwin at first wanted to publish it on Wallace's behalf and to give up his work, but he was persuaded by Lyell and Hooker to allow a summary of his views to be read at a meeting of the Linnean Society, together with Wallace's essay, and both to be published in the Journal of the Society. This was done in 1858.[2] He then wrote *The Origin of Species* and published it in 1859.

[1] T. R. Malthus (1766–1834) was an economist. He published his *Essay on Population* in 1798, in which he put forward the view that, since 'population increases in a geometrical, food in an arithmetical ratio', population is bound to outrun food supply, unless there is some active check to prevent it. He applied the argument to man and was not concerned with the evolution of animals. The application to the theory of evolution was due to Darwin and Wallace. Malthus' argument was not original; it had previously been put forward by Condorcet.

[2] *J. Linn. Soc.*, **3**, 53, 1858.

The publication of '*The Origin*' did not complete Darwin's work on the theory of evolution. In 1868 his book on *The Variation of Animals and Plants under Domestication* appeared. This was important as showing the effects of selection in artificial breeding. In 1871 he published *The Descent of Man and Selection in relation to Sex*. Both these books provided elaboration and confirmation of the theory, but the theory was fully stated in '*The Origin*' and they did not materially add to it. In the second his theory of sexual selection was developed.

Between 1862 and 1881 his minor works on the natural history of animals and plants were published. These included that 'On the Fertilization of Orchids' (1862); 'On the Expression of Emotions in Men and Animals' (1872); 'On the Movements and Habits of Climbing Plants' (1875); 'On the Effects of Cross- and Self-fertilization in the Vegetable Kingdom' (1876); 'On the Different Forms of Flowers on Plants of the Same Species' (1877); 'On the Power of Movement in Plants' (1880); and 'On the Formation of Vegetable Mould through the Action of Worms' (1881). However fascinating most of these books are—and there is nothing in biological literature to exceed the fascination of most of them—they did not greatly add to the theory stated in *The Origin of Species*. They show very clearly that Darwin was at heart a naturalist.

The essentials of Darwin's theory can be very shortly stated.

1. He accepted from Malthus the fact that the reproductive powers of animals are much greater than is required to maintain their numbers. Only if a very large proportion of the offspring are destroyed will the numbers remain constant, as they normally do.

2. If very many individuals are being destroyed, there must be a 'struggle for existence' both between the members of the species and also, since species are often in competition with each other, between species. The struggle for existence will be both intra- and interspecific.

3. Animals vary, and, so he assumed, their variations are inherited.

4. In the struggle for existence the favourable variations will survive and the unfavourable be exterminated. The favourable variations will accumulate, and this 'natural selection' will lead to gradual change in the characters of a species towards better adaptation. This gradual change, when it has proceeded far enough, will result in the origin of a new species. Thus, the means by which evolution, or more accurately the Origin of Species, is produced in nature is explained.

The essentials of the theory can be thus shortly stated; in his book Darwin developed it with a wealth of evidence in its favour. He begins with two chapters in which he demonstrates that variation is a universal property of organisms both under domestication and in nature, and discusses its inheritance. He then proceeds to give in two chapters the evidence for the struggle for existence which he believes to occur in nature. A chapter follows in which he discusses the laws of variability, admitting his ignorance of the basic cause of variation but discussing the types of variation that occur. He then gives chapters to the various difficulties that he realizes the theory will meet, to the variability of instinct and habit, and to the effects of hybridization. These chapters are followed by two on the evidence of the geological record and two on the geographical distribution of animals, showing that in both cases the facts are in accord with belief that species arise by evolution from forms unlike themselves. After a single chapter on the morphological and embryological evidence for evolution, he sums up his views in a conclusion in which the theory is again stated.

Some points in the theory as Darwin put it forward may be mentioned, since they have been important in the later discussion.

1. The belief in the effectiveness of natural selection was a logical deduction from the facts of the life of organisms in nature as Darwin knew them. He had no direct, certainly no experimental, evidence in favour of it. It was an unavoidable conclusion from the conditions of life.

2. He realized that his knowledge of the laws of inheritance was inadequate, and he fairly says so. But this ignorance was not dangerous to his theory. All he required was that some inherited variation should occur, and for this he had plentiful evidence.

3. He believed that natural selection acts mainly on small variations, since it is these that are found everywhere among the individuals of natural populations. Large variations of structure are rare and he thought them less important.

4. He believed that the inheritance of variation was blending, that is to say, that the hybrid between two forms is intermediate between the parents. Later work on genetics has shown that this is not true in the ultimate analysis, and that if it were true organisms would not show the variation that they do show in nature. He did not realize that this is so, but this false assumption does not in any way invalidate the theory.

5. Darwin accepted Lamarck's belief in the inherited effect of characters acquired during the lifetime of the

individual. This he believed was one cause of variation, but he thought that such variation was capricious, and relatively unimportant in evolution.

6. Darwin's conception of the correlation between the parts of the body in structure and function that is necessary if the organism is to remain viable and efficient seems to have been surprisingly incomplete. He speaks of 'correlated variation' but almost always this expression means to him no more than the linking together of variation in two or more parts of the body—as when it is found that hairless dogs always have imperfect feet, or that pigeons with short beaks have small feet. He realized that if a horse evolves longer legs for rapid running its neck must elongate to enable it to graze, but he attributed such correlated change directly to natural selection, which in the horse with longer legs would produce a longer neck. What he did not consider was that large change in any part of the body is impossible, if the animal is to remain viable, without correlated change in many other parts. We shall discuss later the need for this correlation and the means by which it is ensured during evolutionary change (pp. 136-8).

It is strange that there should have been this 'blind spot' in Darwin's outlook. Internal correlation between the parts had been discussed by many biologists from Aristotle onwards. Cuvier had made it the basis of his conception of the organism, and Darwin had read and appreciated his work. It was also inherent in Lamarck's third law, but Darwin could see little good in Lamarck. He says, for instance, in a letter to Hooker[1]—'Heaven forfend me from Lamarck nonsense of a "tendency to progression", "adaptations from the slow willing of animals", etc.!'; and in another place he says that he got

[1] *The Life and letters of C. Darwin*, vol. ii, p. 23.

no single idea from reading Lamarck's work. Perhaps, his dislike of Lamarck's outlook, and his knowledge that internal correlation was inherent in Lamarck's system, predisposed him to disregard it. More probably, he felt that, since he could not understand how such correlation was brought about, it was not a principle that should be given a place in his theory. To this was added the fact that, as a naturalist, his interest was rather in the relations of the organism to the external conditions than in what goes on within the body. We shall come back to this point shortly.

Perhaps, the first impression that is made on a reader of 'The Origin' is the width of Darwin's study of his subject. In the twenty years during which he worked on his theory Darwin had covered all the types of evidence that might be useful to him in putting it forward. He was not very expert in morphology and embryology, and it has generally been thought that the single chapter he gave to those subjects is the weakest part of the book; it was this part that more than any other aroused criticism among the biologists, as we shall see. Where he was discussing the natural history, habits and behaviour of animals there were few among the academic biologists with so wide a knowledge as he, and therefore few capable of criticizing him.

Next, the reader cannot fail to be impressed with Darwin's skill in setting out his material. His literary ability was not great; it was adequate but far below that which, for instance, Huxley showed in his writings in support of Darwin. What Huxley wrote can often be read with enjoyment—the 'People's Lecture' he gave to working men 'On a piece of Chalk', for example. Darwin's writing is always clear—there is never any doubt about what he means—but it is the skill with which he arranged his argument and his immense body of fact that is especially striking. So also is the lucidity of his thought and the fairness and humility of his writing. He is never vague; he scrupulously avoids any appeal to principles which he cannot ascribe to some definite material cause—his outlook is in fact everywhere essentially materialistic. Here he is in very striking contrast to much of the biological writing of the earlier years of the century, some of which has been quoted, that from *The Vestiges of Creation* (p. 38), for instance. Reading him, one gets the impression that he is a scientist of a much more modern type.

Above all, it is his refusal to conceal a difficulty that must impress any reader. Usually indeed he emphasizes a difficulty more than most people would have thought necessary. It may be said that this is skilful writing, for the reader, especially if he is informed, is not usually convinced by overemphasis, disregard of difficulties and polemics; he is more likely to be antagonized. In Darwin it can only be put down to the fairness with which he approached every aspect of his subject.

There is another striking contrast between Darwin's outlook and that of the biologists of the earlier part of the century. The morphologists had not been interested in the life of animals in their environments; their concern had been, as we have seen, with the structural plan of the animal body. The systematists had also been concerned with structure, recording the structural resemblances and differences between organisms. As systematists, Cuvier and Lamarck had been interested in structure, and, when they considered properties of the organism other than its structure, it was the harmony and correlation within the body that give it its nature as a functioning and unitary whole that interested them. Darwin's primary interest was in the organism living its life in its natural environment. He was, as has been said, at heart a naturalist, as also was Wallace. Both of them were instinctively disposed to consider chiefly the effects of external conditions on the animal. This was a clear departure from the biological thought that preceded them. Since evolution is a process occurring in the natural life of animals, it is clearly unlikely that a solution of its problems can be reached if the naturalist's study of animal life is left unconsidered. Other branches of biology are also necessary in the study of evolution, but perhaps none is more valuable than natural history which, in its modern form of ecology, has, as we shall see, been responsible for much of the advance towards solution of evolutionary problems that has been made in recent years.

It is hardly likely that Darwin consciously realized the extreme importance of natural history to a study of evolution and that he laid his emphasis on the relations of the organism to the physical conditions of the environment for that reason. He did so because, as a naturalist, his mind worked that way, and perhaps also because he realized, consciously or subconsciously, that physical conditions in the environment are much more easily investigated than what goes on within the body of the organism. That, at least, was certainly true at the stage to which biological science had reached in his day. In his fear of falling into vague statements not open to investigation—which as we have seen determined his reaction to Lamarck—and in his clear realization that science can only advance where it can investigate phenomena on materialistic lines, we may see other reasons for his preference for studying external rather than internal control of change in organisms.

CHAPTER 5

The Reaction to 'The Origin' among the General Public

DARWIN was lucky not only in the general atmosphere of thought at the time he wrote, but also in writing at a time when a large general public was likely to be interested in his work and was sufficiently informed to appreciate it. His book sold 16,000 copies in England before 1876, and this shows that it was read by a large part of the educated lay public as well as by professional biologists. Probably it was read by more people than would have read it at any time either before or since. Today, 16,000 copies might not be a large sale for a popular book, but it may be doubted whether a book on the theory of biology of the solidity of Darwin's would even today sell so many copies.

The reason for this wide interest is not far to seek. It has already been pointed out (p. 27) that science was popular, and indeed fashionable, in the middle of the nineteenth century owing to the recent and impressive successes of the physical sciences with which the progress of industry was associated. Every town had its Philosophical Society and many were founding their museums. This interest had in the preceding fifty years spread to biology. The middle of the century was the time when Philip Gosse was arranging classes for young ladies to study the biology of the sea-shore, and was finding them profitable; and when naturalists who collected butterflies or snail-shells were much more numerous than they are today. It was also the time when large and beautifully illustrated volumes on birds or mammals were a commercial proposition.[1] The increase of wealth that followed the industrial revolution had resulted in a large moneyed class with the leisure necessary for these interests, and the general interest in science led to their being taken up.

Much of this interest in biology was very amateur, though any intelligent observation of animals and plants soon leads to interest in the conditions of their lives and to appreciation of their biology. Even the collecting of butterflies or beetles, if it extends to more than the commoner forms, leads to study of their natural history and biology. Darwin's arguments were largely founded on facts of natural history upon which this large public could form an opinion, based though it might be on common sense rather than an accurate knowledge of the value of his arguments. Here again he was lucky.

Another reason of a quite different kind made for ready appreciation of Darwin's work by the general public. In England the expansion of industry that followed the industrial revolution was still proceeding. Factories, most of them individually owned, were spreading everywhere in the industrial areas, and the industrialists who owned these factories and worked in them had become numerous and powerful. The doctrine of free trade and the *laissez faire* economics of the Manchester school—based on the thought of the Utilitarians—were generally held to be necessary for the new conditions, except by small minorities of humanitarians such as Lord Shaftesbury. The best man and the best method would always come

---

[1] Lord Templewood (*The Unbroken Thread*, 1949) remarks that his family game-books first show any interest in the natural history of birds at the beginning of the nineteenth century. Previously the interest had been only in the numbers shot. Probably, this interest in natural history largely derived from Gilbert White whose book on 'The Natural History and Antiquities of Selborne' was very widely read.

to the top, so it was held, if nothing were done to neutralize competition. This would be to the general advantage.

Darwin's theory of evolution assumed the universal occurrence of competition between the varieties of organisms; co-operation between organisms played no part in his theory, though today we realize that it also is a real and important phenomenon in natural history. He held that, as the result of competition, living organisms had evolved from the simpler to the more complex in both structure and behaviour, tending towards the condition of the highest animals. If competition has these results in nature, it might surely be assumed that it would have similarly beneficial results in human society. His theory seemed to give an ideal scientific background for the fashionable economic theories of the time. Those who believed in these theories naturally welcomed his conclusions.

Laissez-faire economics were not restricted to England; they were at that time dominant in the thought of most of the countries of the western world. Everywhere this favourable atmosphere for appreciation of Darwin's work existed. In Germany there was yet another circumstance tending to bias opinion in favour of it. This was the spread of Nietzsche's philosophy, with its doctrine of the Super-man, which became fashionable there soon after Darwin wrote. Here, again, Darwin's emphasis on competition gave an ideal scientific and biological background, but here to politics very different from anything Darwin himself supported, for in politics he was a Liberal.

Though Darwin was lucky in many of the circumstances of the time at which he wrote, it is of course true that by no means all the public were ready to accept either the truth of evolution or his views of the means that bring it about. Large sections of the public were not even ready to give them serious consideration, and reacted violently against them. No other scientific work in modern times has stirred so immediate and hostile a reaction from many of the leaders of the thinking world both in England and abroad. Some of the reasons for their hostility are obvious and well-known, but there were other, less obvious, underlying reasons.

First, Darwin's theory was bound to stir up sentimental dislike—sentimental in the sense that it was founded on emotion not argument. This was probably a very general reaction, though by no means the most important in deciding the acceptance or rejection of the theory. Any theory that attributed progress in evolution to competition seemed to imply that nature was everywhere 'red in tooth and claw'. Such a view was bound to stir up antagonism in a public unaccustomed to it, and the fact that Darwin laid no weight on the opposing principle of co-operation between animals probably increased this reaction beyond what it need have been. Many people must have been led by this feeling to hope that Darwin's theory would be shown to be invalid, and to be ready to accept arguments against it. It should not have influenced the biologists, and there is no evidence that it did, but it probably had importance in determining the reaction of parts of the general public.

The most obvious cause of the hostile reaction was the clear contradiction between the story of creation in the first chapter of Genesis and the conditions necessary for evolution if it occurred as Darwin believed it did. This was certainly the most obvious cause of the reaction of churchmen. It has already been said (pp. 23-4) that belief in the complete literal accuracy of the biblical account was still very widely held, and almost all the less-informed churchmen believed that any disproof of its accuracy struck at the roots of religion. That was so in the middle of the nineteenth century when Darwin's work was published, though it is not so clear that this view had been held for very long. Discussing this point in an article on 'Darwin and Religious thought', Father Waggett says:[1]

'Special creation—really a biological rather than a theological conception—seems in its rigid form to have been a recent element even in English biblical orthodoxy. The Middle Ages had no suspicion that religious faith forbad inquiry into the natural origination of the different forms of life . . . So late as the seventeenth century, as we learn not only from the early proceedings of the Royal Society, but from a writer so homely and so regularly pious as Walton, the variation of species and "spontaneous" generations had no theological bearing. . . . It was in the eighteenth century that the harder statement took shape. Something in the precision of that age, its exaltation of law, its cold passion for a stable and measured universe is the occasion for that rigidity of religious thought about the living world that Darwin by accident challenged, or rather by one of those movements of genius, which, Goethe declares, are "elevated above all earthly control".'

Certainly, it can be truly said that it was by accident that Darwin stirred up the furore that followed his publication. He wrote as a biologist hoping to convince biologists. He had no wish to antagonize those who believed in the literal accuracy of Genesis, but he felt bound to state the biological facts as he saw them and to

[1] *Darwin and Modern Science*, 1909, p. 487.

draw the conclusions to which he thought they led. Throughout his life he refused to enter any discussion of the religious implications of his work.

It may be asked why this popular outburst did not occur earlier. The uniformitarian theory of the world's history, as clearly incompatible with the biblical story as the concept of evolution, was stated by Hutton in 1785 and established so far as most scientific opinion was concerned by Lyell in 1830. It may seem strange that the popular reaction did not occur when these scientists published their books. In fact, neither Hutton nor Lyell stirred up an outburst so bitter or on anything like the same scale as Darwin did, though, as has been noted, their views were continually discussed.

Hutton and Lyell were writing on geology, and it may be suggested that this was a less provocative subject than evolution, which concerned animal nature and perhaps, ultimately, man. But those who before Darwin had stated belief in evolution in the living world had caused no general outburst. It is true that in the eighteenth century Buffon had been made to retract his suggestions of evolution before the Sorbonne, and other proofs can be found that the contradiction between a belief in evolution and religious dogma was realized. For instance, Tennyson in 'In Memoriam' has several passages in which he seems to accept as possible not only the geological account of the history of the world but also the animal ancestry of man. But Tennyson was exceptional in that he had followed much more carefully than most what the scientists were doing.[1] He had read *The Vestiges of Creation* and he certainly realized the implications of Lyell's work. He was criticized for his passages in 'In

[1] Cf. Sir Alfred Lyall in *Tennyson and his friends*, edtd. Hallam, Lord Tennyson, 1911, p. 355.

Memoriam' but there was no general outburst against him as there had been none against any of the statements of belief in evolution before Darwin's time.

There were several reasons that the outburst should follow the publication of Darwin's book, some of which have been already mentioned (pp. 58-9). First, the earlier part of the nineteenth century was a time of religious revival especially in protestant England, and this revival had reached its zenith in the eighteen-fifties, almost exactly at the time when Darwin's book was published. The Church in England was more influential than it had been for many years. The revival was largely evangelical, and fundamentalist opinion was general in large parts of the Church. Besides this, religious opinion of the evangelical kind had been shocked by the sermons and writings of the members of the Oxford Movement from the 1830's onwards, and still more by the then recent secessions of Newman, Manning and others to the Roman Church[1]. Religious opinion was not only active at the time and more than usually influential, it was also unusually sensitive to anything that seemed to prejudice the truths in which it believed.

Still another point should be made here. Evangelical opinion in the early nineteenth century was not largely interested in the logical background of its faith; it was concerned more with individual salvation than with theology. Its belief in doctrines such as the literal accuracy of the Bible tended to be dogmatic. When a doctrine based on dogma rather than reasoned argument is opposed, discussion is useless and the reaction is often

---

[1] It may also be noted that the modern criticism of the Bible had started in Germany in the thirties and forties. English opinion was shocked by it and sought to withstand it. Darwin's conclusions seemed to support it.

fiercer than in any reasoned argument. To many of the general public of the Church it was not a question of deciding whether the doctrine of literal accuracy was right or wrong, but of defending a dogma believed to be essential to the Christian religion, and therefore of defending the religion itself.

Then, again, it was probably true that Darwin's book was the first to make the general body of opinion in the world outside science realize the direction in which scientific opinion had moved. The better-informed among the general public had realized earlier that some biologists had expressed belief in evolution, but those who expressed this belief were in fact a small proportion of the biologists, and it must have seemed to many who knew of their statements that their views could be disregarded. The larger part of the general public probably knew nothing of biological opinion on the subject of evolution.

That this was the real position is implied in a letter that Charles Kingsley wrote to Gosse on the publication of his book *Omphalos*.[1] Kingsley admits Gosse's logic, but is shocked, largely because he thinks that the book implies deception on the part of the Creator (*Deus quidem deceptor*) and because he admits he sees no alternative to a belief in evolution other than Gosse's theory. He thinks it may lead many to discredit the story of Genesis and so the whole of scripture—'I would not for a thousand pounds put your book into my children's hands.' He seems to regard evolution as a subject which had not then reached a solution and was better left in the background until science had a firmer case to put forward. This letter was written very shortly before the publication of '*The Origin*'. If Kingsley, both a biologist and a churchman, held that this was the

---

[1] E. Gosse, *Life of Philip Henry Gosse*, 1890, pp. 280–3.

position, we may surely conclude that the greater part of the world at large gave no thought to the possible contradiction between the scientific conclusions and a literal acceptance of the account given in Genesis.

There were other causes in 'The Origin' for the immediate reaction of the theologians besides the evidence it produced against the biblical story of creation. One of these was the conception, by no means new but inherent in Darwin's theory, that man had an animal ancestry. Darwin did not lay stress on this in 'The Origin' but developed it in his *Descent of Man* (1871). It seemed to imply that man should be regarded as nothing more than an evolved animal, a much more fundamental contradiction of orthodox religion than the conflict with Genesis. The popular outburst immediately after 'The Origin' was published was certainly based mainly on the challenge to the literal accuracy of the Bible, but that this second cause of dispute was realized almost as quickly is shown by the fact that it was the subject of Huxley's famous altercation with Bishop Wilberforce at the meeting of the British Association at Oxford in 1860.

The nature of man is a philosophical as much as a religious question, and the part it played in the hostile reaction to Darwin's book may be considered with other and more general philosophical causes of dispute.

It has already been noted (p. 26) that scientific materialism as a theory of all knowledge was spreading in the first half of the nineteenth century. There can be no doubt that the publication of Darwin's work greatly encouraged the extension of materialistic views to biology; and by implication to every kind of knowledge. Darwin himself refused to discuss the philosophic implications of his work, just as he refused to discuss their impact on religion, and he certainly had no wish to be regarded as responsible for them. But his work clearly showed that the whole history of life on the earth was open to investigation by the scientific method. Another part of biology had been brought into the domain of science and, since man was introduced into the story, Darwin's work supported the claim that the whole study of man would in the future form a part of science.

At the time it seemed to those interested in philosophy and religion impossible to accept such conclusions. Today the position is not the same; both sides have modified their views. It has been admitted by many theologians that acceptance of the literal accuracy of the first chapter of Genesis is not essential to religion. Belief in the animal ancestry of man, so far as his body is concerned, is accepted as permissible in the Pope's encyclical *Humani Generis* of 1951. Neither of these causes of dispute were really fundamental to theology, and they were certainly not of fundamental philosophical importance. On the other hand, it was, and still is, impossible for either philosopher or theologian to accept the materialistic philosophy of the scientists as applicable to all knowledge. The claim for the universal extension of materialism may not now be made in its Victorian crudity by the majority of scientists, but at the time it was inevitable that philosophers and theologians should oppose Darwin's theory, since it seemed to support scientific materialism and to extend it outside the range to which it had previously seemed applicable.

Even if scientific materialism were rejected, there were still other fundamental philosophic and religious issues raised by Darwin's theory of evolution, and these alone would have been enough to stimulate determined opposition. They are discussed by Annan in his biography of Leslie Stephen at the point where he is considering Stephen's reason for his loss of faith in Christianity after reading *The Origin of Species*.[1]

In earlier European thought, both religious and metaphysical, God had been regarded not only as a 'transcendental, other-worldly Idea or Ground, self-sufficient, apart from time and space, uniting all eternal ideas, a self-contained perfection, needing nothing to complete or to realize itself', but also as continually active in creation, 'projecting Himself into the Universe'. With the eighteenth-century realization of Progress in nature, the conception was altered by arguing that 'all creatures tend towards God and draw ever nearer to Him during time', but still nature was regarded as an orderly and rational universe under the continual control of divine providence. The requirement of theology to retain the conception of God as continually active in creation had been one of the most fundamental points of dispute between the theologians and scientists in the earlier part of the century. Darwin's book raised it much more directly. Any theory of evolution based on chance occurrences upset all the previously accepted scheme.

Annan says:

'The real significance of *The Origin of Species* lay in its apparent contradiction of orthodox metaphysics. Darwin introduced the idea that *chance* begets order. Fortuitous events, not planned or rational but fortuitous, result in a physical law; the process of natural selection achieved by minute accidental variations in the species, breaks the principle of internal determinism. . . . *The Origin of Species* made the world seem less, not more,

[1] N. G. Annan, *Leslie Stephen*, 1951, pp. 162–6, partly quoting A. O. Lovejoy, *The Great Chain of Being*.

rational, and the universe a creation of blind chance, not a 'block-world' (in William James's phrase) created by an other-worldly Master Mind. . . . Though evolution is almost the least of the problems facing theologians today, Stephen read Darwin as *evidence* that confuted orthodox metaphysics; by using this evidence empirically was it not possible to show scientifically that all metaphysical explanations of the cosmos were worthless?'

We may now think that the conception of material creation as a single act creating a self-regulating and self-evolving system is at least as high a conception as that of a continually active Creator, and that it does not in the least remove rationality from the universe. Even before Darwin wrote, Chambers had maintained this in his *Vestiges of Creation.* Whether this belief is concordant with the Christian beliefs held today is a question we need not discuss. There can be no doubt that this conflict with orthodox metaphysics was another cause of antagonism to Darwin's conclusions. Probably, not only churchmen and philosophers may have felt the antagonism; it may also have lain behind the opposition of many of the more philosophical biologists. We shall have to discuss their reactions in the next chapter.

We may conclude that, when *The Origin of Species* was published, the chief immediate cause of the outburst was the violence it did to the general belief in the literal accuracy of the Bible. Behind that, and irreconcilable so long as scientists maintained their belief in the scientific method as the only source of real knowledge, was the opposition to universal materialism; and with this went the disturbance to traditional views of the nature of the universe and creation. In all these ways Darwin's theories seemed to strike at the foundations of religion and of metaphysics. Much of the conflict was inherent in the intellectual position of the nineteenth century. Sooner or later fundamentalist views were bound to come into conflict with the results of science, and the materialism of the scientists was already disputed by the metaphysicians. Darwin's book gave the shock that brought the conflict to the surface, but, if that shock had not been given, the causes of conflict would still have been there and the dispute would have taken place at some other time. Earlier work in geology and in the theory of evolution had not been well enough known to set off the general reaction. It was Darwin's misfortune, not his fault, that his book did so, partly because it was read by a large public and thus well known, and largely because it brought the living world and even man into the discussion.

So we see that there were powerful forces on both sides of the dispute. The churchmen and much academic opinion were antagonistic to Darwin's views; the more Radical thinkers, many of the scientists and large parts of the lay public were favourable to them. The result of the dispute was decisive. Before Darwin wrote, as we have seen, only a few biologists believed in evolution, and almost none in the one theory—Lamarck's—that had been proposed to account for it. Outside biology the subject was hardly considered except by those few who followed the advances of science. By 1880, not much more than twenty years after the publication of 'The Origin', the large majority of biologists had become convinced of the truth of Darwin's views and acceptance was also very widespread among the general public, though there was still much religious opinion opposed to it. It must be admitted that the speed with which the new theory was accepted was extraordinary.

CHAPTER 6

The Reaction to 'The Origin' among Biologists

To understand the reactions of biologists to Darwin's work it is necessary to realize how great a shock its publication in 1858 and 1859 gave to the biological world. We are so accustomed to belief in evolution as the background of all our biological thought that we do not realize how unexpected was the almost undeniable proof of its truth provided by Darwin from his vast body of evidence of so many kinds—adaptation throughout the living world, the succession of living forms, their geographical distribution, their morphology and embryology and so on. When to all this evidence of the truth of evolution as a fact of nature was added his theory of how it might be brought about, a theory that seemed reasonable and was at least open to discussion, the impression that his work made must have been still more extraordinary. Nor is this all. Evolution, as we have seen, was by no means a new subject. Some biologists had suggested its truth, and Lamarck's theory had been considered and discarded by the biological world. Most had come to the conclusion that no sufficient evidence could be found to convince them that evolution is true. Darwin, by no means one of the leading biologists before his book appeared, had been able to show that the biological world was wrong in this conclusion.

If beauty in science consists, as G. H. Hardy says it does in mathematics,[1] in producing by simple and uncomplicated means results that are fundamental and

[1] *An Apology for a Mathematician.*

novel, then, surely, Darwin's work deserves that attribute as much as Newton's in Physics or any other work in science. For there was nothing original in his collection of evidence for evolution; it could have been collected by any other biologist who had the interest and assiduity needed to do so. Even the principle of Natural Selection was not entirely original; some forecasts of its importance can be found in earlier biological literature,[1] though the principle was probably quite unknown to biologists when Darwin wrote; Darwin himself derived it from thought on Malthus's work, not from earlier biology. Yet from these not very extraordinary premises Darwin produced the fundamental and, to his contemporaries, novel results of his proof of the truth of evolution and his theory of its causation.

There was still another reason why Darwin's work should be received with enthusiasm by biologists, if his deductions could be accepted. This was perhaps the most important reason of all to, at least, the abler biologists. Up to that time biology had been very largely an observational science; animals and plants were described individually in structure and physiology. Only in Lamarck's rejected theory and in the theories of naturphilosophie, which were also by then rejected by most biologists, were the animal and plant kingdoms treated as wholes open to logical analysis. Darwin gave another principle on which biology could be built up into a logical analysis of organic nature, and one much better based. To those who accepted his conclusions, organisms became no longer individual examples of living nature; they became each a part of the single plexus of life evolving through the history of the world. He gave, in

[1] E.g. in the writings of Maupertius in the eighteenth century. Cf. Bentley Glass, *Scient. Amer.*, **193**, 100, 1955.

fact, to biology a logical background. Lamarck's theory and the theories of the natur-philosophers might have done this but they had failed; to most biologists in 1859 there was no such logical background for biology. To provide it in a form that could be accepted by most, and a form that has stood the test of time, was Darwin's greatest gift to biology.

It must not be thought that all or even most biologists immediately acknowledged the truth of evolution. Huxley in an article published in 1887[1] says that he can only call to mind, besides himself, Hooker, Lubbock and, in America, Asa Gray as biologists who declared belief in evolution in the first year. Wallace, who was in Malaya, should clearly be included. There were also others. Darwin in a letter to Hooker dated March 3, 1860[2] quotes fifteen including Lyell (with qualification on the descent of man) and Jukes among the geologists, and Carpenter, the physiologist. Nevertheless, this was certainly a minority of biologists, and there were many especially among the older men who rejected the new views. Owen in London, at Cambridge Darwin's two old teachers Sedgwick and Henslow, and in America L. Agassiz were all opponents both of evolution and of the new theory. All these were elderly men of great reputation. In France and Germany those who at once accepted Darwin's views were even fewer. On the whole we may say that almost all the older biologists and many of the younger were at first against Darwin.

Not all the criticism of 'The Origin' was founded on conservatism and dislike of novelty. Undoubtedly, some of the criticism among the general public was of this nature, and such bias probably played its part even

[1] *Life and Letters of C. Darwin*, edtd. F. Darwin, vol. ii, p. 179.

[2] Ibid., vol. ii, p. 293.

among the biologists. Lyell's refusal to accept the animal ancestry of man seems to have been based on his emotional dislike of that conclusion rather than on argument against it, and other instances could be quoted. But there were many criticisms that were fair and reasoned, and to some of these complete answers have not even yet been given.

A few of the more important of these criticisms may be mentioned:

1. Evolution as we see it in palaeontology and living nature is a gradual, continual and often directional course of change—directional in the sense that it continues in the same direction through many generations and long periods of time. Also, it requires co-ordination of change in many parts of the body; one part cannot change without change in many other organs, if the organism is to remain viable. Darwin, it was said, attributed change to chance variation. Natural selection might be able to give persistent direction to the changes based on these chance variations, but there was no explanation in his theory of the means by which co-ordination was produced. Indeed, as we have seen (p. 51), Darwin hardly realized the need for co-ordination in this sense.

Here we may note Darwin's wisdom in insisting that the variations on which evolution is based must be small. Only small variations could account for the gradual and continuous nature of evolutionary change as seen in fossils, and large and sudden changes are rare in living nature, though they do occur (p. 118). That change is by accumulation of small variations also goes some way to account for co-ordination. An animal responds to alteration in one organ, so long as the alteration is small, by ('phenotypic') alteration in other organs during the

F

individual's life-history—if horns become larger and heavier, the muscles moving the head become stronger; if the animal becomes more active, its lungs and heart may become larger and its respiration may be improved. This is the Principle of Organic Selection that was put forward later in the century by Weismann. By these means the animal may remain viable and survive after small changes, until the appropriate inherited changes occur in the organs in which co-ordinated change is required. The animal could not so react to large and sudden changes of structure or function. These considerations go some way to remove the necessity for simultaneous change in many organs if viability is to be maintained, and therefore to answer the criticism that Darwin's theory did not allow for the need for co-ordinated change.

2. The criticism was made by many that in natural selection Darwin had not proposed a principle governing evolution but only a means by which its failures are eliminated. This is true, and Darwin clearly recognized it. The real basis of evolution in organisms is the occurrence of inherited variation, and Darwin admitted that he knew very little of the causes of variation. That it does occur he knew from observation. Knowledge of the causes of variation had to wait for the advances in genetics during the twentieth century.

That Darwin was fully alive to his lack of knowledge of the causes of inheritance and variation is shown by his attempt to account for them by his theory of Pangenesis,[1] in which he supposed that particles (gemmules) carrying the characters of the organs are thrown off by each organ during the body's life and transmitted to the offspring by way of the gonads. He supposed that these gemmules

---

[1] *Variation of Animals and Plants under Domestication*, 1868, p. 432.

controlled the characters of the body in the new individual of the next generation. The theory is now of no
more than historical interest.

In any case, this criticism is not directed against
Darwin's work. It is merely a statement that his theory
of evolution is not complete, and this Darwin was very
ready to admit.

3. Much of the criticism from continental, and especially German, biologists derived from their outlook
on the science of biology. The German zoologists were
the successors of the school of natur-philosophie, and
still retained much of its outlook, though its extrava-
gances had been discarded. They were still trying not
to interpret the facts of the organism's life in relation to
the world around it but to find a plan hidden in the
structural diversity of organisms. It was therefore natural
that they should object to Darwin's theory by saying
that he had suggested no such plan as they looked for
(Bronn, Kölliker).

That this is a true interpretation of their position is confirmed by Rádl in *The History of Biological Theories*[1].
He says:

'Today, when we look back upon these old criticisms
of Darwin's views and the answers given by his supporters, it soon becomes obvious that here are two opposing
worlds of thought speaking different languages. . . . For
him—Darwin—evolution supplied a *chronicle* of the
universe, full of the smallest incidents: they affirmed
that he had not discovered behind the world's development any great *plan*. By the word *Law* he denoted the
probability with which a definite conclusion can be
deduced from known events: for them Law denoted

---

[1] *The History of Biological Theories* by E. Rádl, transld. E. J. Hatfield,
Oxford, 1930, pp. 63–4.

that external and changeless Law which gives meaning to the manifold variety of nature.'

There can be no doubt that this is important to us in trying to interpret the impact of *'The Origin'*. Undoubtedly Darwin's outlook was quite foreign to those who still retained the fundamental conceptions of natur-philosophie. His outlook was by no means original; it had been held by naturalists and physiologists for many years, and it was exactly the same as that expressed by Lyell in his *Principles of Geology*. It is certainly a more modern outlook. It has become much more generally held in the present century; most biologists now hold it. Perhaps to some extent the prevalence of the German outlook in that country in the middle of the nineteenth century was due to national intellectual characteristics. As we shall see, views that owed their origin to this morphological outlook were still prevalent, not only in Germany but in England and elsewhere, throughout the latter part of the nineteenth century.

One further point should be made here. The German biologists were mistaken in thinking that Darwin's work did not provide biology with a fundamental plan. Evolution itself was such a plan, and, as has already been pointed out, his greatest service to biology was to provide it with this logical and fundamental plan. But it was not the type of plan that the Germans were looking for, and they did not at once appreciate it. Later they accepted it as the basis of their morphological zoology of the latter part of the nineteenth century.

4. As another example of German criticism, that of von Baer may be mentioned. He was now an old man, of very great reputation; his work on embryology was perhaps the greatest German contribution to biology in

the earlier part of the century. He accepted the truth of evolution (as did some others in Germany, e.g. Kölliker); he had indeed expressed belief in it to some extent much earlier (1834). But 'he rejects the theory of natural selection entirely on the ground that evolution, like development, must have an end or purpose (*ziel*)—"a becoming without a purpose is in general unthinkable" ' —here he seems to refer to the contradiction between Darwin's concepts and traditional metaphysics, already discussed (p. 63ff). He points out too the difficulty of explaining the correlation of parts upon the Darwinian hypothesis. His own conception of the evolutionary process is that it is essentially *zielstrebig* or guided by final causes, that it is a true *evolutio* or differentiation, just as individual development is an orderly process from the general to the special.[1]

Clearly, von Baer did not accept the possibility of a completely materialistic biology. To him it seemed impossible that the scientific method could be applied to all biological phenomena. This attitude also was important in determining the reactions of some other German biologists to '*The Origin*'. It was a very different attitude from that of Darwin and his English followers who were interested in using the scientific method as far as it would go, and not interested in determining its limits. That, they felt, could be left to the future, if indeed, as they might have said, such limits existed.

5. Many less general criticisms were made. Of these only a few can be mentioned; most if not all have been subsequently answered.

(*a*) The point was made that it seemed impossible that complex organs such as the vertebrate eye could have arisen by gradual increase of complexity, for in

[1] Quoted from E. S. Russell, *Form and Function*, 1916, p. 242.

the simple forms they must have had in early stages of their evolution they could not have functioned as they now do. An eye would have no selective value for vision by image-formation until it was of great complexity. This criticism neglects the fact that function as well as structure evolves. It can be shown by comparative morphology that the eye originated not as an image-forming organ, but as a simple eye-spot, a group of cells sensitive to light and used for appreciation of the presence or absence of light and nothing more. Its origin in the simple form necessary for that function is not difficult to imagine. Only when it had reached complexity for other reasons did it become capable of forming an image of the external world. This long course of both structural and functional evolution is by no means impossible to understand on the lines suggested by Darwin.

Another criticism against the gradual evolution of complex organs was that small changes in their parts in the course of evolution must destroy their efficiency. This is the same criticism as that concerned with co-ordination everywhere in the body. It is discussed on p. 71.

(b) The objection was made that in development many organs reach complex structure before they begin to function. The vertebrate heart is an example. Since they do not function at the time when their structure is formed, it was said that their development could have no selective value at that time and would therefore not be favoured by natural selection. This objection is removed when it is realized that it is the whole life-history of an animal that evolves. Complex structure in these organs is very necessary when they begin to function, and any failure to develop their structure at earlier stages would undoubtedly have negative selective value.

(c) Darwin's theory of sexual selection was criticized by many. The theory suggested that the secondary sexual characters of animals, the structures and adornments present in one sex but not in both, are evolved because they are attractive to the opposite sex and encourage mating. It met criticism from many biologists, both immediately after its publication and later, chiefly on the ground that the theory was too anthropomorphic; it seemed to suggest that animals had powers of discrimination and even aesthetic appreciation similar to our own. This criticism has been largely supported by more recent work. The view now held is that these characters improve the chance of mating not by influencing choice by the other sex in selecting the mate, but because they stimulate that sex physiologically towards the condition necessary for mating. They do this in association with the displays of mating behaviour so many animals exhibit. This physiological form of the theory avoids the criticism of anthropomorphism that Darwin's theory met.

In spite of criticism of these many different kinds, opinion in favour of Darwin's views spread rapidly. Already, on 2 Dec., 1860, Darwin was able to say in a letter to Huxley:[1] 'Another thing gives me confidence, viz. that some who went half an inch with me now go further, and some who were bitterly opposed are now less bitterly opposed.' In 1865 Kingsley wrote in a letter to F. D. Maurice:[2] 'Darwin is conquering everywhere and rushing in like a flood, by the mere force of truth and fact. The one or two who hold out are forced to try all

[1] *Life and Letters of C. Darwin*, vol. 2, p. 354.
[2] *Life and Letters of C. Kingsley*, 1877, vol. 2, p. 171.

sorts of subterfuges as to fact, or else by invoking the *odium theologicum*. . . ' In 1887 Huxley wrote:[1] 'Even the theologians have almost ceased to pit the plain meaning of Genesis against the no less plain meaning of Nature. . . Genesis is honest to the core, and professes to be no more than it is, a repositary of venerable traditions of unknown origin, claiming no scientific authority and possessing none. . . . As my pen finishes these passages, I can but be amused to think what a terrible hubbub would have been made (and in fact was made) about any similar expressions of opinion a quarter of a century ago. In fact, the contrast between the present condition of public opinion upon the Darwinian question; between the estimation in which Darwin's views are now held in the scientific world (and were then); between the acquiescence, or at least quiescence, of the theologians of the self-respecting order at the present day and the outburst of antagonism on all sides in 1858–9, when the new theory respecting the origin of species first became known to the older generation to which I belong, is so startling that, except for documentary evidence, I should sometimes be inclined to think my memories dreams.'

It is indeed true that by the time of Darwin's death in 1882 his theory had been accepted by the great majority of biologists. Only some of the older generation and some neo-Lamarckians who could not believe that evolution was controlled so largely by conditions external to the organism (p. 88ff) held out against it. Among the general public the movement of opinion in favour of the theory was almost equally general.

[1] *Life and Letters of C. Darwin*, vol. 2, p. 181.

CHAPTER 7

The Later Nineteenth Century

DARWIN took hardly any share in the popularizing of his theory. He disliked controversy and hardly ever engaged in it. He lived a quiet family life at his house at Downe continuing his biological work, writing his later books, and keeping up a large correspondence with biologists both in England and abroad. In England the major part of the work of popularization fell upon Huxley, though many others took part in it. In Germany Huxley's place was taken by Haeckel.

Huxley was a younger man than Darwin; he was born in 1825. He had spent four years (1846–50) cruising in the seas round Australia as the naturalist on the *Rattlesnake*, a naval ship sent on a surveying expedition to the Great Barrier Reef and New Guinea. Like Darwin, he was therefore a man who knew animals in their natural environments, though he was by training more of a morphologist than Darwin was, and throughout his life his outlook was more that of an academic zoologist than Darwin's. He accepted the fact of evolution and in large part the theory of natural selection immediately on the publication of '*The Origin*'. But his acceptance was not complete; even to the end of his life he did not agree that species could arise by selection of small variations alone. Nevertheless, he threw himself at once into the fight for Darwin's views and up to his death in 1895 he was the protagonist of the fight in England. For that rôle he was particularly well suited. His reputation as a leading biologist was great; he had

before the publication of '*The Origin*' written a monograph on the medusae which made his reputation, and
he continued to publish much zoological work throughout his life. He held for many years professorships in
London, and was thus able to represent the new views
in academic zoology. Also, he enjoyed polemics, was a
fine speaker, and had the ability to write effectively and
indeed finely. Besides all this, he was greatly interested
in extending education among the general public;
many of his lectures to Philosophical Societies, Institutes
and other bodies are still readable. His ability in putting
the problems of evolution before the general public
was especially valuable. Darwin was very lucky in
finding such a champion to propagate his views.

Haeckel, though the counterpart in Germany of Huxley
in England, was not in all ways like him. He had been
bred up as a morphologist of the old German school that
derived from natur-philosophie. His earliest works
were a text-book of *General Morphology* (1860)—with
Gegenbaur, another leading German morphologist—and
his monograph on the Radiolaria (1862). Though he had
travelled, he had not the training as a naturalist that
Darwin and Huxley had, but he accepted the theory of
natural selection immediately on reading '*The Origin*',
and fought for it for the rest of his life. The Darwinian
standpoint is already present in his *General Morphology*,
but his most influential book was *The Riddle of the
Universe* which followed in 1866. In his evolutionary
theory he was more completely in agreement with Darwin than Huxley was; he accepted in fact the argument
of '*The Origin*' in full.

Haeckel's importance is much more as a combatant
for evolution than as an original thinker in biology. His
chief theoretical contribution was his theory of Recapit-

ulation, in which animals are supposed to evolve by addition of new stages of the life-history at the end of development—a tadpole represents the fish ancestor of the frog, and the frog is a new developmental stage added to the life-history. This was a return to the theory of the natur-philosophers Meckel and Serres who held similar views early in the century; it was a denial of the conclusions of von Baer (p. 18). The theory of re-capitulation was almost universally accepted by biologists in the latter part of the century, but in the last fifty years it has not stood the test of the advance of knowledge and is now discarded by most.

In his propaganda for Darwinian views Haeckel was as successful as Huxley; their spread was almost as rapid in Germany as in England and by 1880 the great majority of German biologists accepted them.

One reason for the spread of Darwin's views among biologists was that many of the suggestions made by Darwin were confirmed by biological work in the years that followed 1858. Some were surprisingly soon proved right. He suggested, for instance, that birds evolved from reptiles, and in 1859 the criticism that there was no definite evidence for this was easy. In 1862 the fossil *Archaeopteryx*, which combines many features of reptiles and birds, and is indeed one of the best intermediate forms in all zoology, was found in the Jurassic Solen-hofen slates of Bavaria, and in 1872 the toothed birds *Hesperornis* and *Ichthyornis* were found in the Creta-ceous of Kansas. Darwin's suggestion was thus fully confirmed. Hofmeister's work on the reproduction of lycopods and other plants belongs to the sixties and seventies of the last century, and showed evolutionary connection between phanerogams and lower plants. Marsh's evidence of the evolution of horses based on a long series of fossil forms found in America, and many other examples all confirming the truth of evolution could be cited. If a theory contains truth, evidence in favour of it may be expected to accumulate as time goes on. Darwin's theory was certainly so supported, and at a rate that greatly helped to persuade biologists of the truth of the theory.

At first sight it may seem surprising that very little of the biology of the second half of the century was on the lines of Darwin's own work. With some exceptions that will be mentioned later, hardly anyone tried to carry his conclusions about the theory of evolution farther—the evidence for evolution was greatly expanded, but Darwin's theory of it hardly at all modified. Even the study of the natural history and biology of organisms, such as filled Darwin's smaller books, occupied an altogether minor position in the biological thought of the time. Work of all kinds was actively carried on but the dominant outlook of the leading zoologists was morphological, and this was especially true of the academic zoologists of the universities. Their studies of morphology were very different in outlook from most of Darwin's work. Only his study of the cirripedes was morphological, and even this was concerned with their systematics and biology as well as with their morphology.

It was perhaps natural that study of the theory of evolution should be neglected as that time. Darwin's book had caused so great a disturbance of the outlook of biologists that time was needed for re-adjustment, and it was felt that his work had carried the theory as far as the knowledge of the time would allow. It seemed likely that further work of that kind would be unprofitable.

This was not the only reason for the dominance of the

morphological outlook in these years. It had other, mainly historical, causes. The kind of morphology that was dominant may be called morphological phylogeny. It consisted of study of the structure of animals and plants with the object of deducing from the knowledge so gained their evolutionary relationships, and so working out the course that evolution has followed in the animal kingdom. Both the adult structure and the embryology of the animals were studied, and the phylogenetic conclusions drawn from the work were largely supported by palaeontological evidence provided by study of fossils. By the end of the century the relationships of the groups of animals and plants to each other may be said to have been determined, at any rate in broad outline, and phylogenetic trees of the major groups could be drawn. There can be no doubt that this morphological study of animals and plants is an essential part of the science of evolutionary biology—biologists must always be interested in the course of evolution and in the reasons for similarities in structure among organisms. But this does not explain why it became so dominant in the later nineteenth century. Its dominance was most complete in zoology—in the eighties and nineties it was regarded, at least in England, as almost the only kind of zoology worthy of work in a university laboratory. In botany it was less dominant; physiological work on plants was continued throughout the period. The physiology of animals was regarded as the business of departments of Physiology, where, in most universities, it was studied with a medical bias. Systematics was the business of the museums, and natural history and observation of animals in the wild the business of amateurs. As an example of the feeling in a zoological department the reply to a request for support for appointment to a lectureship that

Bateson got from Sedgwick[1] at Cambridge in 1890, when he was working on his *Materials for the Study of Variation* (published in 1894, and referred to later [p. 103] as one of the starting-points of the study of variation in the twentieth century) may be quoted. In a letter Bateson writes[2]: 'Sedgwick tells me that he would not wish me to have Weldon's lectureship if W. goes to University College. He says, as I expected, that I have gone too far afield'—from morphological work— 'and that my things are a "fancy subject".'

It is not hard to see why biology, and especially zoology, developed on these lines in the latter part of the century. We have already noted (pp. 20, 37) that the zoology of the first half of the century was mainly morphological where it was not purely descriptive. It was not likely that the zoologists who followed Darwin, being at heart morphologists, would readily turn to work in natural history. Also their morphology, in Germany and largely elsewhere, being developed from natur-philosophie, retained the basic idea that zoology must be aimed at finding a plan underlying the diversity of organisms. To them the conception of zoology as a study of animal life as it is lived today was entirely foreign. To accept it seemed to be to give up the aim of developing zoology as a logical science. It is not surprising that they retained their basic idea of a search for a plan, and modified their outlook only so far as acceptance of evolution forced them. The nature of the plan to be looked for was altered—instead of the purely hypothetical arche-typal plans of natur-philosophie (p. 17) it became the plan of evolutionary descent—but the idea of a search for

[1] Zoologist of Cambridge, later Professor of Zoology, not Darwin's friend (p. 44).

[2] *William Bateson, F.R.S. Naturalist*, 1928, p. 42.

a plan was not abandoned. Phylogenetic morphology was thus in direct descent from the morphology of the early nineteenth century. Darwin was able to convince the zoological world of the truth of evolution, but he was not able to divert the general body of zoologists from their morphological outlook to the study of the life of animals, his own chief interest.

That this morphological outlook dominated the period is, then, a natural result of the history of the subject. That its dominance was as complete as it was is not surprising. The older zoologists of the time having been brought up in morphological ideas before the publication of Darwin's book, the younger men followed them. Until the end of the century, Germany was undoubtedly still the centre of morphological zoology, but in England there were also many morphologists. Owen, who never accepted evolution, was the leading English zoologist at the time of the publication of '*The Origin*' and continued his morphological work for many years thereafter. Balfour, Ray Lankester, Sedgwick and many others were younger men who devoted their lives to evolutionary morphology. In France and America the dominance of this type of morphology was almost as marked as in Germany and England.

The dominance of morphology did not prevent some few advances in the theory of evolution. In most cases these were concerned with subsidiary deductions rather than with the essentials of the theory.

For instance, in 1862 H. W. Bates suggested[1] mimicry as the cause of the extraordinary resemblances in colour and pattern between species often distantly related to each other—a species not itself distasteful to predators by coming to resemble another species that was distaste-

[1] *Trans. Linn. Soc.*, **23**.

ful shared the advantage of the distastefulness. The
resemblance was therefore increased and perfected under
natural selection. In 1879 another explanation of some
forms of mimicry was suggested by Fritz Müller[1]. He
had observed in South America groups of species,
especially among butterflies, which showed similarities
of colour and pattern in all the species of the group. He
suggested that these common plans in the appearance of
species would be of advantage if the species were distasteful, since a predator would learn the single pattern
of the group more rapidly than a separate pattern for
each species. Work of all kinds on mimicry was continued actively throughout the remainder of the century
by Poulton and others. It was work of very much the
same kind as that set out by Darwin in his smaller books.

There was also much work on the geographical distribution of animals, in which A. R. Wallace took a large
part. Evidence that the facts of distribution were in
agreement with what was to be expected on the theory of
evolution was collected. In his book on *Island Life*
Wallace described the faunas of oceanic islands, showing
that their relative poverty could be explained by the
difficulty of reaching the islands across the sea, and the
large proportion of peculiar species in island faunas
could be ascribed to evolution on the island after arrival.
Distribution gave further evidence when considered together with the results of geology. The absence of
indigenous placental mammals from Australia and the
peculiarities of the South American mammalian fauna
were explained by separation of these continents from
the other land masses of the world for long geological
periods. Palaeontology also gave evidence of the course
of evolution.

[1] *Kosmos*, 1879, p. 100.

One major modification of the theory took place in these years. This resulted from Weismann's recognition (1885) of the separateness of the gonad from the rest of the body, the soma.[1] He pointed out that the gonad, though resident in the body and dependent on it for food and maintenance, is otherwise independent; it may indeed be regarded as in the position of a parasite on the soma. This relationship of soma and gonad, undeniable when once pointed out, made the possibility of any form of Lamarckian inheritance very difficult to credit. Unless some such theory as Darwin's pangenesis (p. 72) was accepted—and there was no evidence for such a theory—it was very difficult to believe that an 'acquired character' could alter the hereditary material in the gonad and so be inherited by the next generation. From the time of Weismann's papers the almost universal disbelief among biologists in Lamarckian inheritance dates. From this time Darwin's acceptance of Lamarckian inheritance as a subsidiary cause of evolution was discarded by the great majority of his followers.

So far we have considered mainly the biologists who accepted Darwin's theory. They were the great majority, but there were still some who were unable to accept the theory. After 1880, only a few of the oldest men—Owen for example—still refused to accept the truth of evolution as a fact of nature. Most believed in evolution and many who rejected the theory of natural selection tried to find some other explanation. Of these the most interesting were those who developed theories of evolution related to a greater or less extent to the theory of Lamarck. Their views were not at all influential among the general body of biologists—who rejected any form of Lamarck-

---

[1] *Die Kontinuität des Keim-plasmas*, 1885. The idea may be found in earlier writings of biologists, but it is here set out in a very clear form.

G

ism on the grounds put forward by Weismann—but their outlook on the problems of evolution was very different from that of Darwin and his followers, and their views deserve mention here. They may be called neo-Lamarckians.

Darwin had based his theory on the observed fact of variation in organisms. He also believed that the variation was undirectional, occurring in all directions and not more in one direction than in others. For him the directional character of the organism's evolution was due to the action of natural selection, that is to say to the action of conditions external to the animal, and not to the organism's own exertions or to anything going on in the body.

To some, especially psychologists and students of behaviour in the higher animals, this seemed to neglect the active, kinetic, nature of the organism; to neglect its essential characteristic of being a moving, behaving, reacting system. They thought that Darwin dealt with the organism far too much as if it were inert, at the mercy of the conditions of the environment, unable to react against them and so to protect itself. Evolution, they thought, must be an active process within the organism, and its course must also be determined within the organism and not by conditions outside it. It is not necessary for us to discuss here whether these criticisms have any weight. We shall come back to them in a later chapter (p.190). Even most of the neo-Lamarckians admitted natural selection as a negative process with the function of removing the inefficient, and there can be no question that Darwin's explanation of the directional character of evolution by the action of natural selection was entirely logical. The criticisms of the neo-Lamarckians derive much more from a different outlook on the nature of the living organism and on the way in which its life is likely to be controlled, than from disagreement about fact or, sometimes at least, from denial that Darwin's theory might be a theoretically possible solution. That it was the true solution they were unable to believe.

The neo-Lamarckians fell back on Lamarck's theory of the inheritance of acquired characters but they modified it variously. In one form or another they maintained that the organism's own exertions determined the direction of variation, and therefore its evolution. Since the effects of activity can only influence the evolution of the race if they are inherited and passed on to the next generation, all such theories are necessarily Lamarckian. Also, they all lack any background of observation; no clear evidence was ever brought forward that the effects of activity are in fact inherited.

Several such theories were proposed in the latter part of the nineteenth century and the first decade of the twentieth. Samuel Butler regarded all structure and all physiology as the result of ancestral experience recorded in the organism as what he called unconscious memories. As the experience becomes older, he believed the performance of the acts associated with it become more and more unconscious. Circulation, breathing and speech in man are in order of decreasing evolutionary age and increasing conscious control. Cope, the American palaeontologist, and Semon in Germany also produced theories of neo-Lamarckian type.

In their lack of supporting evidence these theories seemed to the general body of biologists to have no place in a scientific theory of evolution. No biologist can fail to realize that the organism is a kinetic and not a static system, and it may certainly seem surprising at first sight that Darwin's theory, which gives no place to the organism's own activities in the causation of evolution, should be as successful as it appeared to be. But this was due to Darwin's refusal to discuss the cause of variation which is, as he fully admitted, the necessary basis of any evolutionary change. Now that we have more knowledge of variation we know that variation is not, so far as we know, directly caused by the organism's activities during its life-history. The neo-Lamarckian theories receive no support from this new knowledge, but our present theories are by no means complete and the question whether Lamarckian heredity may still have some part in the causation of evolution cannot be so easily decided. We shall consider again later whether it has (pp.191-2).

So we reach the end of the nineteenth century and may summarize the position at that time. Forty years had passed since Darwin set out his theory. In that time it had been accepted by general opinion both in science and, though less universally, among the lay public. There was still fundamentalist opposition to any belief in evolution, as there still is half a century later, but this opposition had lost much of its influence among the better-informed part of the public. The acrimonious disputes that followed the publication of '*The Origin*' had largely died down. Many of the theologians had come to realize that the literal accuracy of Genesis is not essential to religion. They were still bound to oppose any general materialist philosophy, and to deny that the scientific method is the only sound means of gaining knowledge. But some of the scientists were beginning to modify their claims to the universality of their method, and in the new century this retreat from complete materialism has gone further. Where agreement was still not possible, much of the heat had gone out of the conflict, and the combatants were often ready to agree to differ rather than to dispute the subjects of disagreement fiercely.

In biology both the fact of evolution and the theory of natural selection as its cause had become accepted as almost unquestionable truth for all except a few small minorities of biologists. One cannot read the writings of the time without realizing that discussions of these subjects seemed to most biologists no longer required, and that anyone who questioned their truth could only be either ignorant or prejudiced. The theory was accepted by almost all except the few neo-Lamarckians as a dogma of biology. We shall see in the next chapter that this confidence was by no means soundly based; it was largely lost in the first few years of the new century. But in the eighties and nineties of the nineteenth century this was undoubtedly the generally accepted position for almost all biologists.

Apart from the disbelief in Lamarckism that resulted from acceptance of Weismann's theory of soma and gonad, and from the development of the theory of mimicry, evolution by natural selection was accepted at the end of the century in a form that differed hardly at all from that enunciated by Darwin. Pangenesis was not accepted but this was no part of Darwin's essential theory. It was put forward by him only as a possible basis for Lamarckism, unsupported by evidence.

Perhaps no better proof of the soundness and brilliance of Darwin's work can be given than the fact that the large amount of biological study in the latter part of the century led to so little modification of his theory, for biology of all kinds had advanced actively in these years.

Histological study of the cell had given very important results which were at the base of the advances of the new century, but these results did not earlier give rise to any modifications of the theory; embryology, palaeontology and the study of geographical distribution only confirmed his conclusions; morphological phylogeny and systematics were based on them.

In spite of this activity in many branches of biology, academic zoology was still predominantly morphological and phylogenetic in outlook. Study of the conditions governing animal and plant life in nature was regarded as a side-line rather than as a main aim of biology. But there were already signs towards the end of the century that this dominance of morphology might soon decrease. In Germany Driesch and Roux were beginning in the late eighties and in the nineties their experimental study of the development of the individual organism which went much further in the new century. In America also study of the animal's life as it is lived today was becoming active. In England, though some were engaged on biological work that was not morphological—Poulton, for instance, was working on mimicry, and Bateson on the study of variation that led him to genetics—the predominant position of morphology in academic zoology was still unchallenged. In botany the dominance of morphology having never been as great as in zoology, the outlook at the end of the century was much less restricted than that of the zoologists.

PART II

The Twentieth Century

CHAPTER 8

The Turn of the Century

IF 1858 is a cardinal date in the study of evolution, 1900 is almost equally cardinal, for it was in that year that Mendel's investigation of heredity was rediscovered. On his work, and the conclusions to which it led him, the progress in the study of evolution during the last half century has been based. That progress is the subject of the following chapters.

There is another reason why the year 1900 is a turning point in the history of our subject. So far one aim of this book has been to give some account of the interplay between the development of biological ideas concerning evolution and thought outside science. Up to the end of the nineteenth century demonstration of the truth of evolution as a fact of nature played almost as large a part in discussions of the subject as development of the theory in explanation of it. But the fact of evolution had by the end of the century become generally accepted, both among biologists and, in very large part, among the lay public. Evolutionary ideas had made their impact on man's thought, and this was true not only of the concepts of biological evolution. As a result of the discussion of evolution in biology, the conception of evolutionary change in all nature had deeply penetrated the thought of the time. Consciousness of change in the world of nature had certainly been present in earlier periods but it had probably never been so near the surface of men's minds as it had now come to be. It was much less easy to argue as if the conditions of life, human or other, were static and could be maintained without change.

The truth of evolution being accepted, discussion among biologists has from this point onwards been mainly concerned with the means by which evolution is brought about. This is a question for biologists rather than for the lay public. In the nineteenth century, it is true, the details of Darwin's theory had greatly interested the public because they seemed to accord so well with the then fashionable economic theories, but, even then, the public was quite as much interested in the reasons that forced acceptance of the truth of evolution as in its theory. In the present century there has not been the same reason to expect lay interest in evolutionary theory, and still less reason to expect it in the modifications of the theory which have been found necessary to bring it into line with the results of modern biology. At times during the last fifty years, when biologists have disagreed openly in their views on the theory of evolution, public interest has revived, especially when it was thought—wrongly—that the biologist's disagreement implied doubt of the truth that evolution has occurred, but, in the main, public interest in the subject has been less than in the last century.

From this turning point onwards our discussions must be aimed mainly at tracing the development of the theory of evolution as it has been modified in accordance with the advance of biology, and not so much at defining its interactions with thought outside biology. Nevertheless, the history is still of great interest. It provides a good example of how a scientific theory may become modified in time by the accretion of new fact; how these new facts may at one time seem to deny the fundamental truth of the theory and later lead back to it; and especially how separate lines of investigation, dealing with the subject matter of the theory from different points of view, may at first seem to give entirely contradictory results but may later come into accord with each other, so that the contradiction is removed.

The Darwinian theory of evolution in the form accepted by the biologists of the 1890's had more than one weak side. These weaknesses were to become important in the discussions of the following years, but until they were brought into the open by the results of new work they were unrecognized; in the 1890's biologists had no idea that their theory was in any way weak. The following weak points are evident now, though they were not evident to them.

1. The lack of any direct evidence of the effectiveness of natural selection in nature was a definite weakness. Darwin had believed it to be effective as a logical deduction from the facts of reproduction and of the general constancy of numbers in populations of organisms. Selection *must* be effective, he said, if so many are born and so few reproduce. Before the 1890's, it had often been pointed out that a great deal of the death-rate of animals is undeniably non-selective. A cod may lay two million eggs in a year, and of these not more than one or two survive to form the population of the next generation. Those that die before reaching the reproductive age are destroyed by being eaten by animals or in other ways in which the characters they bear almost always play no part in determining their fate; whether they survive or not is for the vast majority decided by chance. It is, however, clear that the existence of much chance mortality is no good argument against the effectiveness of selection. Whether selection is effective does not depend

on whether those that survive are a large or small proportion of the eggs that are laid—the great majority of
cod's eggs that die non-selectively may simply be written
off, so far as the reproduction of the fish is concerned;
it depends on whether possession of characters of selective value is more frequent among those that survive to
the reproductive age than it would have been in the
absence of selection, that is to say, on whether selection
is potent *among the survivors*. This is a complete answer
to the argument that much of the mortality of animals in
nature is non-selective, but it does not touch the question
whether there is any real reason to believe in the effectiveness of selection in any circumstances, in this case
among the survivors. Unless selection is effective,
Darwin's theory clearly breaks down.

Many of Darwin's followers of the nineties would
have said that the fact of adaptation in organisms to the
conditions of their life proves the effectiveness of selection, but that argument cannot be maintained. It is valid
only if Darwin's theory is accepted, if the basis of
evolutionary change is that postulated by him—variation
non-directional in its origin but giving rise to directional
change under the influence of selection. If that is not
the true basis, adaptation can arise from other causes.
If, for instance, Lamarck was right and the direction of
evolutionary change is determined by the organism's
own activities, selection is not required to account for
adaptation. Nor is it required on any theory of special
creation.

Even if Darwin's theory is accepted on the grounds
of its logic—and it is hard to avoid the logic of his argument—there can be no doubt that the position would
have been much strengthened by direct evidence that
effective selection does occur in nature. At the end of

the nineteenth century there was hardly any irrefutable evidence of this. Some attempts to provide it had been made but it cannot be said that their results were sound enough to do much more than confirm the beliefs of those who were already believers. Further, there was no knowledge of the conditions necessary for selection to be effective. It was not known, for instance, how large a selective advantage must be for selection in its favour to be effective. Nor was it known whether selection is equally effective in all the conditions of life that organisms live, equally effective in plants and animals, in communal and solitary life, in communities reproducing bisexually or asexually, and so on.

One consideration at least should have cast doubt on belief in selection as a universal determinant of evolutionary change. It is extremely hard to believe that *all* the characters of organisms have selective value. Particularly, this is true of the small, trivial characters that distinguish closely related species and sub-species from each other. It needs very great faith to believe that the differences in form of the leaves of two species of oak, or the exact forms of the spots on the wings of two closely-related species of moth have any real effect on the survival of the species.   But, if they have not, the biologist of the nineties should have been forced to conclude that selection cannot be responsible for their present forms[1], and that Darwin's theory gives no explanation of their origin and preservation in the specific form. They are not in general more variable than other characters that may well have selective value; often they are less variable.

Thus it is clear that the theory of natural selection in

[1] It has later been held that such characters are genetically linked with other characters which are of selective value, and that they are preserved because these other characters are preserved by selection.

the form in which Darwin left it, which was still the form accepted at the end of the nineteenth century, was at least incomplete. Darwin's work had made it very probable that selection is a potent force in nature and is responsible for much of the directiveness of evolutionary change. Almost all biologists thought this undeniable, and looking back few would disagree with them today. But it is now clear that little more than this could be said. Much work was needed before a sound and general account of the effectiveness of selection could be given.

2. Before the 1890's there had been little observation of the detailed course of evolution even in the very early stages where small differences are evolved. Darwin had given evidence that organisms isolated in small areas out of contact with the rest of the species become differentiated—the finches of the Galapagos Islands, for example, and the land-snails of Madeira—and had used this evidence in proof that evolution occurs. But the manner in which these differences arise, the course by which they develop, the speed of their development, and how far it is modified by the conditions of the organism's life, were unknown. Observations of the course of evolution in living organisms were hardly possible, for the rate of change is presumably so slow that many generations would have to be observed before any definite conclusions could be reached. No decisive observations of this kind have been made today.

There is, however, another source from which evidence of the actual course of evolution may be gained. In the sedimentary rocks series of strata lying conformably over each other without change in the type of sedimentation are occasionally found, and it may reasonably be inferred that these strata were laid down continuously without intermissions. In these strata we can trace the history of a fauna through the whole period of the sedimentation, a much longer period than any for which we can observe living organisms. We can thus observe the course of evolution during this relatively long period.

At the close of the century work of this kind was beginning; it has been carried much further in more recent years. An example of early work is that of Rowe[1] on sea-urchins of the genus *Micraster* in a series of strata of the Chalk of England. The type of evolution he found is illustrated in Fig. 1, in which two forms from the

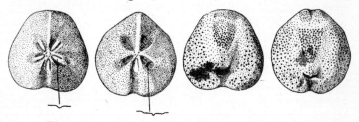

Fig. 1. Evolution in the Genus Micraster (Afer Rowe).

bottom and top of the series of strata are shown. Even in a series such as this, the change is not large, but it is clear. It is, first of all, gradual; there are no large jumps from one form to another, and the closer the strata are to each other the more similar are the sea-urchins in them. The change therefore results from a succession of very minute changes following one another throughout the whole period of the sedimentation. Secondly, the change is directional—it proceeds in the same direction throughout the period—and forms from intermediate strata are intermediate in form. Thirdly, the change takes place simultaneously in many parts of the body; in the figure it can be see in the outline of the body, the

[1] Rowe, A. W., *Quar. J. geol. Soc.*, London, **55**, 494, 1899.

shape of the mouth, and the form of the grooves on the aboral surface of the body, the ambulacra. Intermediate stages showed that all these characters changed simultaneously, not successively. These conclusions have been confirmed by similar work in later years.

In fact, the type of evolution Rowe found was exactly that which Darwin believed to occur. From this time, it should have been clear that Darwin was right in his conceptions of the type of change that constitutes evolution in the early stages and results in the origin of new species, but before the 1890's Darwinian theory lacked the support of these observations. Whether the larger differences of evolution, those that distinguish large groups of organisms, arise in the same way as the small differences to be seen in these series is a question to which we must return later (Ch. 14).

3. The most obvious gap in the theory of evolution accepted at the end of the nineteenth century was the almost complete ignorance at that time of the laws of inheritance. Galton had published earlier the results of a statistical study of inheritance in man[1]. He had shown that variations of the kinds that occur in human populations are inherited, though incompletely; there was always a tendency for the offspring to regress towards the mean. He found that the deviation of the offspring from the mean, in such a character as height, was on the average one-half that of the parent; if a man was 4 inches taller than the mean, his child was on the average 2 inches taller. This was expressed by saying that there was a regression of 50 per cent. Many characters, both physical and intellectual, were studied. From his results Galton was able to deduce his 'law' that the characters of the individual are determined as to one half by those of

[1] Galton, F. *Hereditary Genius*, 1869; *Natural Inheritance*, 1889.

his two parents, one quarter by those of his four grand-parents, one eighth by those of his eight great-grand-parents, and so on.

This work was greatly extended towards the end of the century, both on man and other organisms, by Karl Pearson and his school. Its service to the development of the theory of evolution was to show that at least some of the variations that commonly occur in populations of organisms is inherited and is therefore available for the action of selection.

In the 1890's some other biologists had begun to study variation on very different lines from those of Galton and Pearson. In 1894 Bateson published his *Materials for the Study of Variation.* He had been disturbed by the lack of knowledge of heredity at the time and hoped to approach the study of heredity through that of variation. He was impressed with the fact that in nature many species are differentiated by strongly marked characters and not by quantitative differences such as those studied by Galton and Pearson. He therefore considered that large varia-tions might be important in evolution, in spite of Darwin's belief to the contrary, and he decided to study such large variations. In his book he described in great detail and in many animals the large variations, some of them better called abnormalities, that occasionally occur —variations in the number of segments in the vertebral column or in the number of digits in the hand or foot, modifications of the colour pattern in insects, and so on. Such variations are rare—they are never present in more than a small proportion of a population of a species—and are clearly distinct in kind from the normal quantita-tive variation between all the members of a population, in such characters as size or weight, which Galton and Pearson studied. Bateson's variations may be distin-

H

guished as '*discontinuous*' variations, from the '*continous*' variations of Galton and Pearson. Bateson believed that discontinuous variation is at least as important in evolution as continuous variation. The distinction between continuous and discontinuous variation was important in later discussions of evolution.

In 1901 de Vries published the results he had obtained in experiments on the evening primrose, *Oenothera Lamarckiana*.[1] Though published just after the end of the century, this work dealt with the nature of variation and may be considered here. de Vries found that in breeding this plant he obtained numerous distinct forms, many new to him, all of which arose by sudden, and apparently single, large changes in the form of the plant. He called these changes '*mutations*', and, like Bateson, he put forward the view that evolution takes place, at least partly, through discontinuous variations such as these—which after they had arisen would be subject to selection—and not through continuous variation. There was thus in the conclusions of both Bateson and de Vries contradiction not only to the results of Galton and Pearson but also to the direct observations of the palaeontologists on the faunas of series of strata. We shall find that this contradiction played a large part in the discussions of the following years.

One other piece of work, which was also published after the end of the century, may, since it is concerned with the nature of variation, be considered here. This is the work of Johannsen on variation in self-fertilized populations of beans.[2] He found that he could separate

[1] *Die Mutations-Theorie*, 1901. Since its publication the work has been much criticized. We are here concerned only with de Vries' conclusions, not with the soundness of the work.

[2] *Uber Erblichkeit in Populationen und Reinen Linien*, Jena, 1903.

each population into a large number of lines which differed in many characters, often quite small. Since the plants were self-fertilized, there was no opportunity for crossing between the lines, and he found that the characters of each line bred true in successive generations. But the individuals within each line were not identical; they differed from each other in various other small characters. These differences were however not inherited and he came to the conclusion that they were due to the action of conditions of the environment external to the plant during its life-history. They were, in fact, acquired characters of the kind that we have discussed in considering the Lamarckian theories. Such variation is often called *phenotypic*.

All the variation with which Johannsen dealt was clearly of the kind that we have called continuous; the variations occurred generally throughout the whole population, and they were small and quantitative rather than large, discontinuous variations. His work established that the continuous variation of populations of organisms includes two kinds of variational change. One part due to the action of the environment on the individual is not inherited, at any rate in experiments such as his, which dealt with only a few generations; the second part consists of small inheritable variations.

We may conclude, from all this work, that the variations of organisms may be classified, first, into continuous and discontinuous variation, and that within continuous variation part is inheritable and part not. Whether discontinuous variation or that part of continuous variation that is inherited provides the material on which selection acts in evolution was at the time with which we are dealing disputed. Many biologists impressed by the evidence that Darwin had brought forward, and by that of the palaeontologists, believed that the changes of evolution were produced by selection acting on the small differences of continuous variation; others, such as Bateson and de Vries, gave at least equal importance to the large changes of discontinuous variation. It was a notable feature of the position at the turn of the century that the possibility that discontinuous variation might be important as a basis for evolution had become emphasized for the first time since the publication of *The Origin of Species*.

In 1900 the position was greatly altered by the rediscovery of Mendel's work on inheritance. This discovery forms the subject of the next chapter.

CHAPTER 9

Mendel's Experiments on Inheritance

GREGOR JOHANN MENDEL was born in 1822. He spent his adult life as a monk of the Monastery at Brünn, then in Austrian Silesia, now in Czecho-Slovakia. After 1868, he was abbot of his monastery. From 1853 to 1868 he taught natural science at the school of the monastery, and it was during those years that most of his experiments were carried out. They were continued until 1873, but after that year his duties as abbot prevented his going on with them. He published some of his results in the Transactions of the Brünn Natural History Society in 1866, but many are only known from his letters to the German botanist Nägeli. He died in 1884.

Mendel's results are so fundamental to the more recent advances in the study of evolution that it will be worth-while to give an account of them in some detail.

The most striking feature of Mendel's work is the care and clarity with which he thought out his experiments and selected his material. Before his time many biologists had hybridized plants, and some had crossed animals, but their work had given no clear conclusions on the manner in which characters of the body are inherited. Mendel believed that this failure was because the earlier observers had considered the inheritance of general appearance rather than that of single characters, and had worked with populations of organisms rather than with individuals. He therefore decided to breed from two individuals differing in a single marked character and find out how this character was inherited in the offspring. He realized that the following character-istics of the material would make his experiments easier and the results more certain:

1. The animals or plants should be easily bred through several generations.

2. The varieties forming the parent stocks should differ in well-defined characters.

3. The parent stocks should breed true for the characters in which they differed.

4. It should be easy to prevent fertilization other-wise than intended in the experiments.

5. The hybrids between the parent stocks should be fertile.

Being mainly a botanist, most of his experiments were carried out on plants. He used for his longest set of experiments the common pea, *Pisum sativum*, which satisfied very well the conditions he required. He was able to find many varieties differing in such characters as the height of the plant, the colour of the flower or seed, the position of the flower, and so on. In preliminary experiments he showed that the varieties bred true. The hybrids were fertile and he was able to prevent chance fertilization by covering the flowers in paper bags.

In one set of experiments he chose the height of the plant as the character to be investigated. He crossed a tall race, the plants of which grew to about 6 ft., with a short race in which the plants were not more than $1\frac{1}{2}$ ft. high[1], and found that the first hybrid generation were all as tall as the tall race. The direction of the cross, i.e. whether the male or female parent was tall,

---

[1] It is important to note the difference between these variations, and all those Mendel worked with, and continuous variations such as those in height in man. Mendel's variations were *between*, not *within* populations, and there were no intermediates between the variational forms. Cf. p. 132.

made no difference. Nor did the direction make a difference in any other of his experiments. He then crossed these hybrid plants (called the F_1 generation) among themselves and found that in the next generation (F_2) both tall and short plants occurred but no intermediates. The tall plants were about three times as numerous as the short. Self-fertilizing the plants of this, F_2, generation, he found that the short plants and one-third of the tall plants bred true. The other two-thirds of the tall plants gave the same results as his cross-fertilizations of the F_1 generation, tall and short in the proportion of approximately 3 : 1, and again the tall plants could be divided into one-third that bred true and two-thirds that gave talls and shorts in the proportion of about 3 : 1. These results were confirmed in experiments in which he used other characters in the parent stocks.

From the results of these simple experiments he was able to deduce all the essential points of his explanation of the mechanism of heredity.

1. The characters are handed on from one generation to another unchanged. Intermediates do not occur, and there is no blending of the characters with each other. However long the breeding is continued, they remain as distinct as they were in the original stocks. Therefore, their development in the individual plant must be controlled by some element, or 'factor', which passes through the fertilizations unchanged.

2. Since the F_1 generation was able to produce short plants when they were cross-fertilized among themselves, they must have contained a factor for shortness although they were themselves tall and had therefore also the factor for tallness. Presumably the factor for shortness came from their short parent. In

all his experiments he found one character of a pair expressed in the F_1 generation, and this character is called 'dominant'. The other character of the pair which was not expressed, though the factor for it was present in the plants, is called 'recessive'.

3. Fertilization consists in the fusion of two cells—gametes—one from each of the two parents. These must contain the factors controlling the development of the characters of the plant, and the individual must contain a double set of these factors, one set from each gamete. The parent stocks always bred true, showing no sign of containing the opposing characters of a pair, so that both sets of the factors contained in them must have been those for the characters expressed in their bodies.

We may thus represent the parent stocks as ● ● and ○ ○, where ● and ○ are symbols for hereditary material containing the factors for tallness and shortness respectively. The F_1 generation, since it gets its hereditary material from both parents will be symbolized as ● ○.

When gametes are produced by the F_1 generation, we may suppose that these factors will separate, and equal numbers of gametes bearing the factors for tallness and shortness will be formed. These will meet indiscriminately at the fertilization when these plants are cross-fertilized, and we may expect to get plants of the following constitutions:

a. ● ●—which will be tall and will breed true as did the tall parent stock.

b. ● ○—which will be similar to the plants of the F_1 generation, tall plants giving tall and shorts in the proportion of 3 : 1 on self fertilization.

c. ○ ●—which will be identical with the plants of
type *b*.

d. ○ ○—which will be short plants breeding true
and of the same type as the short parent
stock.

The whole experiment may be diagrammatically
expressed in the following scheme:

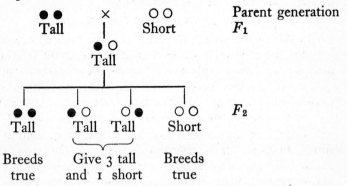

This theory, which Mendel developed, fits so exactly
the results of the experiments, as well as being in accord
with our knowledge of the facts of fertilization, that,
even on this evidence alone, there could be little doubt
of its truth. However, Mendel was able to confirm it by
crossing plants of the F_1 generation with each of the
parent stocks. If his theory is correct, we should expect
the following results:

a. Crossing F_1 with the tall parent,

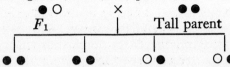

All should be tall and one-half of them should breed
true.

b. Crossing F_1 with the short parent,

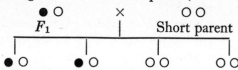

Half should be tall and half short, and the short but not the tall plants should breed true.

He obtained the results predicted by the theory.

Mendel went much farther in his investigations. Besides using several other characters in races of the pea, he also bred and crossed some other plants, and got in every case except some experiments with the hawkweed, *Hieracium*, results in agreement with those that we have considered. His experiments on the hawkweed and the reasons for his failure to get similar results in them will be mentioned later. He also crossed plants differing not in one pair of characters but in two or three. As an example of these experiments we may take those in which a race of peas with round and yellow seeds were crossed with another race in which the seeds were wrinkled and green.

The F_1 generation had round and yellow seeds. Roundness and yellow colour are therefore dominant. On crossing these F_1 hybrids among themselves, he found that all the possible combinations of the characters occurred in the F_2, and in proportions approximately those to be expected on the scheme deduced from his experiments with a single pair of characters. What these proportions should be can be easily determined. If we use the symbol R for the dominant round character and w for the recessive wrinkled, Y for the dominant yellow colour and g for green, the parents will be represented $RRYY$ and $wwgg$. Their gametes will be

RY and wg, and the F_1 generation will be $RwYg$. This will produce four kinds of gametes RY, Rg, wY, wg, and at fertilization these will meet in the combinations given in the following table:

RY	RY	RY	RY
RY	Rg	wY	wg
Rg	Rg	Rg	Rg
RY	Rg	wY	wg
wY	wY	wY	wY
RY	Rg	wY	wg
wg	wg	wg	wg
RY	Rg	wY	wg

Since R and Y are dominant, all those among these combinations that contain R will have round seeds and all that contain Y will have yellow seeds. Those that contain R and Y (9) will have round and yellow seeds; those with R but not Y (3) will have round and green seeds; those with Y but not R (3) will have wrinkled and yellow seeds; and those with neither R nor Y (1) wrinkled and green seeds. The proportions should therefore be $9 : 3 : 3 : 1$. Mendel's results were as nearly as could be expected in agreement with these expectations.

The case in which the parents differ in three pairs of characters can be worked out in a similar way. There are then 8 different types in F_2, and they should occur in the proportions $27 : 9 : 9 : 9 : 3 : 3 : 3 : 1$. In some experiments Mendel obtained approximately these proportions.

Besides confirming the theory deduced from the simpler experiments with a single pair of characters, these results were important in giving proof that different sets of characters are inherited independently. This must be so if they are able to appear in every possible combination in the products of crossing.

When Mendel's results were published in the Transactions of the Brünn Natural History Society in 1866, they did not attract any general interest in spite of the fact that his work was known to Nägeli, one of the leading German botanists. At this Mendel was disappointed. He was also disappointed by the results of the experiments he did on the hawkweed, *Hieracium*. Crossing in this plant was much more difficult than in the pea, owing to the form of the flower, and he found that, when he succeeded in making crosses, all the F_1 hybrids seemed to breed true, differing therein essentially from the behaviour of the peas and the other plants he worked with. This has later been shown to be due to the occurrence of parthenogenesis in the hawkweed, the seeds developing without fertilization: he had not produced any effective hybridizations. Mendel knew nothing of this. Perhaps partly because of these disappointments, and partly because he had less free time as abbot, he discontinued his experiments.

His work remained unknown to biologists in general until it was rediscovered almost simultaneously in 1900 by de Vries in Holland, Correns in Germany and Tschermak in Austria.

So far as the theory of evolution is concerned, the really important conclusions established by Mendel are the following:

1. Characters of the kind that he worked with, of large effect in the body of the organism, and without intermediates, such as the height of a plant or the

colour of its seeds, may be inherited as single and unitary 'factors' in the hereditary material of the organism.

2. These factors are inherited independently, so that they may appear in hybrids in any combination.

3. One of the characters of a contrasting pair may be dominant to the other, and will be expressed in the body of a hybrid although this also carries the hereditary factor for the other (recessive) character of the pair.

4. When hybrids bearing the hereditary factors for both members of a pair of characters are bred together, both the characters appear in the next generation in proportions that can be predicted from the theory that the gametes each bear the factor for only one member of a pair, whereas the individual after fertilization—the zygote—bears two factors, and that the gametes meet indiscriminately at fertilization. The factors are said to 'segregate' in the gametes. (A zygote in which the two factors of a pair are identical is called a *homozygote*; one in which they differ, as in the F_1 generation of Mendel's experiments, is called a *heterozygote*.)

5. There is no blending in the inheritance of the characters. No intermediates occur in the hybrids and the characters remain stable and unchanged through an indefinite number of generations. In later work it has been found that the heterozygotic F_1 hybrid may often be intermediate between the parent forms. This is known as *incomplete dominance*. It is not due to any blending of the characters for in the F_2 generation they appear again in the same forms as in the original parents. Rather it is due to the action of both factors in the body of the hybrid. In some crosses the hybrid may be very different in form from either parent—the 'blue' Andalusian fowl is a hybrid between the very different black and white forms of the parents.

CHAPTER 10

Early Genetics

IN discussing Bateson's book on variation (p. 103), we
noted that he held the view that evolution advances
rather by large and sudden changes in the heredity of
organisms than by the summation of small changes, as
Darwin believed, and as the changes in the fossil faunas
of palaeontological series seemed to show. In de Vries'
work, on *Oenothera* (p. 104), published almost at the turn
of the century, also, the emphasis was on large and sudden changes and not on the summation of small changes.
When Mendel's work was rediscovered in 1900, it
seemed to fit in well with the views of these workers in
that he found that large differences between races might
be inherited as single units and, presumably, might
therefore arise as single changes at one step. It is thus not
at all surprising that the rediscovery of his work was
received with enthusiasm by those who had been thinking along these lines.

Very soon after its rediscovery Mendel's work was
confirmed and extended widely. Characters of very many
kinds both in animals and plants were found to be inherited in a 'Mendelian' manner. Not only structural
characters of all kinds, from large abnormalities like the
absence of the wings in insects or the great reduction of
the tail in the 'rumpless' fowl to smaller differences in
colour pattern or the structure of feathers, behaved in
this way. Some physiological abnormalities such as night-
blindness in man and even an abnormal type of behaviour,
waltzing in Japanese mice, also did so. The sexual differ-

ence in many organisms was found to have a Mendelian basis.

Sometimes a factor was found to modify characters in more than one part of the body, having 'multiple effects', and sometimes more than one factor might control the characters of a single part or organ—the form of the comb in the cock was found to be influenced by at least two factors—but in general it was found that the factors produced different and independent effects, and each part of the body seemed to be controlled by one or at most a few factors. There thus grew up the belief that, in the control of the characters of the body by a large number of these factors, they exerted their control in a mosaic manner, each factor, or a few factors, controlling the properties of a part of the body or one of its physiological or behavioural functions. This, the *'mosaic theory'* of the action of the factors, became widely held.

Histological work in the nineteenth century had shown that there are present in the cells of the body, both in animals and plants, rod-shaped particles, the chromosomes, definite in number in each species but differing among the species from 4 to more than 100; and that these chromosomes divide very exactly along their length at each normal division of the cell. In contrast, in the production of the gametes it was found that at one division the chromosomes did not so divide but passed over bodily into one or other of the gametes, so that their number in the gamete is reduced to one-half that in the other cells of the body. The number is restored to that in the cells of the parent when the two gametes fuse at fertilization.

Very soon after the rediscovery of Mendel's work the exact parallel between the behaviour of the chromosomes and that of his hereditary factors—as shown in the diagrams given in the last chapter—was noticed. Both factors and chromosomes are present in double number in the body of the parent, they are both reduced to half this number in the gamete, and restored to the double number at fertilization. It was therefore suggested at first that the chromosomes might themselves be the Mendelian factors, and later, when the factors were found to be more numerous than the chromosomes, that the factors were carried as smaller bodies within the chromosomes. Later work has, as we shall see, established this as a certainty, but at the time it was no more than a reasonable hypothesis. These factors within the chromosomes were called '*genes*', and the whole assemblage of genes in the body of an organism its '*genotype*'.

This hypothesis of the presence of the factors in the chromosomes received support when it was found that some factors, when present together in an organism, do not segregate in the F_2 generation but remain associated, acting in fact as a single factor. On the hypothesis they should behave so if they are contained in the same chromosome, for parts of the chromosomes do not normally separate in the division of a cell or in the development of the gametes; the chromosome divides longitudinally when it does divide and whole halves separate. All the genes in a chromosome should therefore keep together in hybridization; they should be unable to segregate.

Lastly, sudden alterations in the factors of the genotype of an organism were observed. They were called *mutations* since it then seemed that the new forms de Vries observed in *Oenothera* were due to changes of this kind. These mutations were rare; it has been shown in later work that a single gene does not normally mutate in more than 1 in 100,000 of the individuals of a population, and often in less. There seemed to be no correlation between the occurrence of a mutation and any condition of the environment that might have caused it, and no correlation between the effects in the body of successive mutations in a race of organisms. When a mutation had occurred, it was found that it behaved in hybridization with the parent form in just the way that Mendel had found the differences between his parent races to behave in his experiments. On this evidence it seemed clear that differences of the kinds that Mendel used must have arisen by mutations of this type.

Evolution is a process of change in the heredity of organisms, and if it is based at all on the factors of Mendelian heredity, it is on mutation that its progress must depend. The nature of the mutations and their occurrence is therefore especially important to us in our discussion of the cause of evolution. It is worth-while to amplify the account given in the last paragraph by quoting what R. C. Punnett says of mutations in the sweet pea.[1]

'From what we know of the history of the various strains of sweet peas one thing stands out clearly. The new character does not arise from a pre-existing variety by any process of gradual selection, conscious or otherwise. It turns up suddenly complete in itself, and therefore it can be associated by crossing with other existing characters to produce a gamut of new varieties. If, for example, the character of hooding in the standard'—the upright petal of the flower, the upper part of which is bent forwards in the hooded form—'suddenly turned up in a family such as that shown in Plate IV'—a family of seven colour varieties—'we should get a hooded form corresponding to each of the forms with the erect standard; in other words, the arrival of the new form would

[1] *Mendelism*, 5th ed., 1919, p. 78.

I

give us the possibility of fourteen varieties instead of seven. As we know, the hooded character already exists. It is recessive to the erect standard . . . It is largely by keeping his eyes open and seizing upon such sports'— mutations were at first called 'sports'—'for crossing purposes that the horticulturist "improves" the plants with which he deals. How these sports or *mutations* come about we can at present but surmise.'

We do not yet know certainly the causes of mutations in nature. But it is clear that those with which the early geneticists worked were rare and sudden, produced large changes in the body as the result of a single unitary change in the heredity, and that there was no correlation between the changes produced by one of these mutations and those produced by a second mutation that followed the first.

Now, we have seen (p. 50) that Darwin believed that evolution proceeded by the accumulation of small changes under the action of selection. He based this view not on the need for continued correlation throughout the evolution—as he might have done (pp. 71-2)—but on his knowledge of animals in nature, on his experience that closely related forms differ in small divergencies in many parts of the body, the extent of the differences being inversely proportional to the closeness of the relatedness of the forms. We have also seen that Darwin's opinion received support when the changes that occur in the faunas of palaeontological series—e.g. Rowe's *Micrasters* (p. 101)—were observed. It is clear that in such series the changes are gradual, continuous and directional, and occur in many parts of the body simultaneously.

To naturalists, palaeontologists and many others it seemed impossible that the large mutations with which the geneticists were working could give rise under the action of selection to changes of the type they could observe in evolving faunas and floras. At least in the early stages of evolution—which were all that they could study—it seemed that these mutations had no place; it appeared that evolution must be based on some other type of change in the heredity of organisms. The nature of this other type of change was undetermined, but it seemed much more probable that small inherited variations of the kind that Johannsen had found in the continuous variation of his populations of beans might, under selection, give evolution of the kind they observed.

On the other hand, the geneticists pointed out that their mutations were the only kind of inherited change that had been accurately investigated. They, like other biologists, were unable to believe that mutations of this kind could form the raw material on which selection could work to give evolution according to the Darwinian theory. They maintained not that evolution must be based on some other form of heredity but that the whole theory of evolution by the action of natural selection must be given up. Many regarded the means by which evolution is brought about as again an entirely open question, though hardly any denied the fact that evolution does occur in nature.

There thus arose a direct antithesis between the views of the geneticists and those of biologists of many other kinds. The debate was carried on, often acrimoniously, throughout the first quarter of the twentieth century. Two different lines of approach to the problems of evolution had produced results that seemed in direct conflict with each other. They have been brought into agreement only in the last thirty years.

A somewhat extreme example of the views of the

geneticists is given in Bateson's Presidential Address to the British Association in Australia in 1914.

Bateson begins by admitting the fact of evolution. He also admits that natural selection is of undeniable effectiveness in weeding out inefficient whole organisms, but he says that 'to find value in all definiteness of parts and functions . . . is mere eighteenth-century optimism.' Even Darwinians may admit that not all the features of organisms are necessarily of value (p. 99). He then says that 'variation from step to step must occur by addition or loss of a factor', and that these are inherited in a Mendelian manner. There is here the assumption that the steps are large, for he says that there is no evidence of the summation of small factors to give large changes. It is this that forces him to conclude that the Darwinian theory breaks down, since it assumes the summation of small hereditary changes under the action of natural selection. It is particularly the random and rare occurrence of Mendelian mutations—the fact that a second mutation has no correlation with a first in the type of change that it causes in the body—that makes summation impossible.

Bateson goes on to say that most mutations are degenerative; they represent loss of characters and not gain of new characters. Even when they appear to give rise to new characters—as in dominant white coloration or in new arrangements of colour, e.g. in pied rabbits or picotee sweet-peas—he believes the mutation is more likely loss of an inhibitor than truly the gain of a new character. He doubts whether new characters are *ever* formed by mutation, and is forced to suggest a full-bodied pre-formation theory of evolution—that the characters of all organisms were present from the start of evolution and the progress of evolution is wholly due to their becoming expressed in the bodies of organisms. Few will be able to follow him here (cf.p. 182). Beyond this he refuses to give any theory of evolution.

Not all geneticists took so extreme a view as Bateson. For instance, de Vries stated his conclusions in the following sentences[1]:

'Thus we see that the theory of the origin of species by means of natural selection is quite independent of the question, how the variations to be selected arise. They may arise slowly, from simple fluctuations,'—i.e. continuous variation—'or suddenly, by mutations; in both cases natural selection will take hold of them, will multiply them if they are beneficial, and in the course of time accumulate them, so as to produce that great diversity of organic life, which we so highly admire.'

Nevertheless, there is no doubt that views similar to Bateson's were widely held among biologists, even by many who were not primarily geneticists. Thus, we find D. H. Scott, a botanist, expressing his position as follows even at a considerably later date (1921) than Bateson's address[2]:

'It may be that the theory of natural selection will one day come into its own again . . . But in our present total ignorance of'—the causes of—'variation and doubt as to other means of change, we can form no clear idea of the material on which selection has had to work and we must let the question rest.

'For the moment at least the Darwinian period is past: we can no longer enjoy the comfortable assurance, which once satisfied so many of us, that the main problem had been solved—all is again in the melting pot. By

[1] *Darwin and Modern Science*, edtd. A. C. Seward, 1909, p. 84.

[2] Presidential Address of the Botanical Section, *Brit. Assn. Report*, 1921.

now, in fact, a new generation has grown up that knows not Darwin.'

Many examples could be given of opinion on the other side. Thus Tate Regan, a zoological systematist, in his Presidential Address to the Zoological Section of the British Association in 1925[1] discusses Johannes Schmidt's observations on variation in the viviparous blenny, *Zoarces viviparus*[2]. In fiords in Denmark this fish was found to be distributed in populations separated from each other, and in each population characters were found to vary about a mean value, the curves of distribution about the mean differing slightly from one population to another. There was not the least sign of separation of the individuals into groups carrying or not carrying large Mendelian mutations. And it cannot be said that such variation is environmental and not hereditary. Galton, for instance, had shown that variation of just this type is inherited in man. It is also the same type of variation as that found in evolving palaeontological series.

Tate Regan concludes:[3] 'Darwin has been criticized, because, we are told, he did not know that there were two sorts of variations—mutations, which are inherited, and fluctuations, which vary about a mean and are not inherited. But when you point out to a mutationist that the inheritance of many fluctuating[4] variations has been proved—parents above the mean, for example, giving offspring above the mean—he tells you that that shows that the variation is not really fluctuating, but only apparently so, and that a large number of factors must be involved. This is in effect a complete withdrawal, for

[1] *Rept. Brit. Assn. Adv. Sci.*, 1925, p. 75.

[2] *J. Gen.*, vii, p. 105, 1918; x, p. 179, 1920.

[3] Ibid, p. 84.

[4] Here 'fluctuating' is used in the sense of 'continuous' (p. 104).

it amounts to an admission that Darwin was right if he considered that these types of variation differed only in size and frequency.'

Looking back, we can see that there were really two points at issue. First, there was the question whether the Mendelian scheme applied to all inherited differences between organisms, not only to the large mutational changes that formed the material for the experiments of the geneticists, but also to the smaller differences responsible for continuous variation in so far as it is hereditable. On this point there was relatively little discussion, for the evidence available at the time was concerned only with the larger mutations of the geneticists. Secondly, there was the question whether evolutionary change resulted from large and sudden mutations or from accumulation of the smaller differences of continuous variation. This was the main question in dispute. It was Bateson's belief that large mutations were the only possible material for progress in evolution that made him declare against the theory of natural selection in his Presidential Address. It was their knowledge of the types of variation and evolutionary change that occur in natural populations that forced all those who dealt with animals or plants in the field rather than in the garden or the laboratory to the opposite conclusion. The antithesis was complete and in the early 1920's the study of evolution seemed to have reached a blank wall beyond which for the moment advance was impossible. How this antithesis has been resolved is the subject of the following chapters.

Genetics was a new and fashionable branch of biology. Bateson's authority was great, and his address received much publicity not only among biologists but also among the general public. Many, and probably most, biologists agreed with him that Darwin's theory needed to be greatly modified before it could be brought into line with recent knowledge of heredity—that in fact, as Scott said, the subject was again in the melting pot. The reactions of the general public were more extreme and equally important. Fundamentalist opposition to belief in evolution had not entirely died out—indeed it has not today— and Bateson's statements were avidly seized upon not only as criticisms of the Darwinian theory but as implying doubt of the truth of evolution. There was nothing in the address to imply this—Bateson, in fact, states clearly his belief in evolution—and, as has been said, no considerable biological opinion has doubted its truth in the present century. But the fact that biologists were engaged in controversy on the problems of evolution shook many of the lay public from the acceptance of the fact of evolution that had become almost general by the end of the nineteenth century. Even today the results of these controversies are to be seen in the lay attitude to the problems of evolution, for public opinion changes slowly unless it is stirred by some outstanding and striking event. We still find many of those who have not followed the more recent biological work maintaining that the theory of natural selection has been disproved and is now rejected by biologists. Sometimes it is still said that biologists have given up any firm belief that evolution has taken place, and in support of this the writings of twenty-five or thirty years ago are quoted.

CHAPTER II

The Last Thirty Years—Genetics

THE progress of evolutionary theory in the last thirty years is a complex subject, for the new knowledge which has contributed to the progress is of many different kinds. Almost every branch of biology has provided evidence that has played some part in the advance, and a general change in our whole biological outlook has been perhaps even more important than accumulation of the details of biological knowledge. In two branches of biology this change of outlook has been especially striking. One of these is genetics, in which the changes in our views of the genotype and its mode of action in the body has done more than anything else to resolve the deadlock which, as we saw in the last chapter, the study of evolution had reached thirty years ago; and the other is the study of the conditions in which life is carried on in its natural environments, the study of ecology. It is now realized much more clearly than before that evolution is not primarily a change in the structure and physiology of organisms, but rather a change in their whole life as it is lived in nature, and that structural and physiological change accompanies, and is often the result of, changes of life and habit. It is clear that we can have no sound theory to account for evolution unless we know the conditions under which organisms live their natural lives.

Many other types of biological work have also contributed to the progress of the study of evolution in the last thirty years—study of the changes that occur in the individual's life-history in evolution, mathematical study of how selection works on variations of the kinds allowed by genetic theory, experimental and observational study of the action of selection in nature, further study of palaeontological series, and so on.

Most of this recent work has been concentrated on explanation of the smaller changes of evolution in which differences are evolved up to the stage of the formation of new species—often called *micro-evolution*. These small changes set the fundamental problem on evolution; Darwin realized this, and showed that he did so in the title of his book. All evolution is based in micro-evolution, though the larger changes may, and do, present additional problems. We have today reached a far more satisfactory interpretation of these small evolutionary changes than of the larger changes. That is to be expected since we have far better opportunities of studying them. Study of the large changes, *macro-evolution*, must necessarily be slower.

In this chapter we will consider the recent development of genetic theory in its relation to the advance of the theory of micro-evolution, leaving the newer views of ecology and selection to the next chapter. We can then in a third chapter, summarize the interpretation of micro-evolution to which these facts lead. After that we may pass on to discuss the larger evolutionary changes.

The modern work on genetics has been immensely detailed and elaborate. It has been concentrated especially on analysis of the genotype of the fly *Drosophila*, which was found to be in many ways particularly suitable for the analysis. This work, started by T. H. Morgan in 1909 and continued ever since, has given us a most detailed knowledge of the structure of the genotype in that animal and of the mutations that occur in it. On

Drosophila, in fact, our whole modern conception of genetics has been founded, but the main conclusions have been confirmed in other organisms and the general picture to which they lead must be accepted as undoubtedly true of all animals and plants.

Fortunately, we do not need for our present purpose to discuss the greater part of this work. We may assume the proof, now undeniable, that the genes lie in the chromosomes (pp. 117-8) as discrete bodies, and that their locations there are definite, so that maps of the chromosomes giving the positions of the genes may be prepared. Nor need we discuss the evidence that mutation may consist not only in change in the genes themselves but also in alteration of their arrangement in the chromosomes. Further, we need not discuss the details of the behaviour of the genes in the division of the cell and in the preparation of the gametes for fertilization. All these subjects have been closely investigated in the modern work on genetics.

For us it is the change of outlook on the manner in which the genes act in controlling the characters of the body that is the most important feature in the recent history of genetics, and particularly the complete rejection of the earlier mosaic theory (p. 117), in which single or at most a few genes were supposed to control each organ of the body, more or less without interference from other genes. More recent evidence has shown that such a view must be entirely discarded. Many genes do certainly produce their largest effects each on some one organ—the colour of the eye in *Drosophila* is controlled in this way by several genes—and the genes are generally named by these '*primary*' effects. But the primary effect of any gene is modified by mutation in many other genes. Perhaps, at least potentially, it may be modified by mutation in any other gene of the genotype, though the effects of many of the genes may be unrecognizably small. We must conclude that the character of each organ is controlled not by one or a few genes but certainly by a large number, and perhaps by all the genes, which interact with each other to give the character that the organ assumes in the body. It is the genotype as a whole that controls the character of each organ, not any individual genes.

That so many genes act on each organ should not be surprising, for the whole complex of genes of the genotype is present in every cell of the body and therefore in each of its organs. It would be much more surprising if the genes acted as they were supposed to act when the mosaic theory was accepted.

The essential feature of this new conception of gene action is realization of the complexity of the interactions between genes in producing their effects in the body. Their interactions are of many different kinds. Not only positive or negative modification of the extent of the action of a mutation—so that in one condition of the rest of the genotype it may produce a very large effect and in another condition a small or even unrecognizable effect—but many other types of interaction occur. The action of a mutation may be entirely inhibited by mutation in another gene, or its effect may not be expressed in the body unless mutation in a second gene also occurs; mutations in two genes may produce different effects on the same organ but when both are present only the effect of one is seen, that of the other being inhibited; and mutations in two or more genes that have the same effect may, when more than one is present, produce no larger an effect than one of these mutations. Also, there are found to be many genes that have no primary effects but act only by modifying the action of genes of larger effect. The effects of these '*modifying genes*' are almost always individually small, but they are very numerous and the action of a mutation may be greatly altered by the whole complex of them. It is true that these modifying genes of small expression are largely hypothetical —they have not in general been located in the chromosomes and it is probable that mutations in them are due rather to small re-arrangements of the genes in the chromosomes than to changes in the genes themselves (p. 129) —but it seems that the facts of natural variation, and some experimental evidence, leave no doubt of their reality. In point of fact, all genes are hypothetical in the sense that they have not been directly observed. So also are atoms or electrons, but the indirect evidence for the reality of both electrons and genes is so great as to be overwhelming.

We must conclude, then, that the whole genotype acts in every part of the body to determine the character of each organ and each physiological process. In so doing the genotype acts as a unity, but changes in any of its constituent genes may produce change in the action of the genotype.

If this is the true nature of the genotype and its action in the body, what are the results to be expected in the variability of populations of animals or plants? Suppose that we have a mutation in the cow which produces a longer horn in the animal carrying it than in the normal cows of the population. That, of course, will be inherited as a unitary, all-or-none effect in the Mendelian manner, as Bateson conceived. But the expression of this mutation in the body of any cow, the actual length of the horn, will vary with the condition of the many other genes in the genotype that modify the expression of this mutation;

by mutation in these other genes the expression may well be varied from extreme length to a length hardly at all different from that of the horns of cows that do not carry the mutation. Mutations in these other genes will also each be inherited in the all-or-none Mendelian manner, but they are many, and differences in them also many, so many in fact that in natural populations it is probable that no two individuals are alike in all the genes of the genotype; and the result to be expected from the large number of differences in them is that the expression of the mutation for long horn should vary continuously from a very slight lengthening of the horn to production of a horn of extreme length. Between these extremes the horns should grade evenly in a quantitative manner.

This is what we should expect when a large new mutation appears in a population, but it should also be seen in the variability of characters in a population in which no large new mutation has appeared. Since all individuals of natural populations differ among themselves in numerous genes, the expression in each part of the body will vary in this graded manner. It can, in fact, be shown mathematically that each character should vary about a mean in a 'curve of error', variations decreasing in frequency with their distance from the mean.

It is found that the great majority of characters in organisms show this type of variation. Size in man is one such. We know well enough that men are not tall or short in the way that Mendel's peas were. If the heights of a population of men are plotted on a graph, they give a curve of error (Fig. 2) with a mean of about 69 inches, the numbers of individuals falling off on each side as they differ more and more from the mean. The population grades regularly from the very short to the tall. This is because height in man is not controlled, as that of Mendel's peas was, by mutation in a single gene, but by a large number of the genes of the genotype. Each of these genes is presumably inherited in the Mendelian manner and the effect of each is all-or-none, but this character of their effects is obscured since they all act on the same character and their effects overlap.

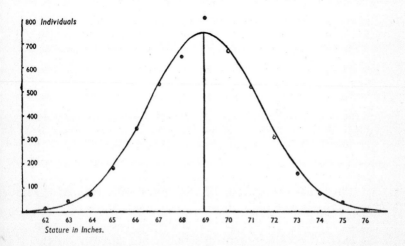

FIG. 2. Variation in stature of a large number of members of Cambridge University of British Extraction.

So it is with almost every character in natural populations. Occasionally we find large differences between the individuals of natural populations that segregate in the Mendelian manner and are caused by differences in single genes. One such is the black coloration which has spread in industrial districts of England and Western Europe in the populations of several species of moth. In at least one species this has been shown to be due to a single mutation. Other instances could be quoted. But that type of variation is rare. It is undeniably true that races and species in nature differ very largely, and indeed almost entirely, in characters controlled by differences in large numbers of genes. We can show that this is so by crossing two races. If their differences were controlled by single genes, they should segregate in the F_2 generation in the Mendelian proportions of $1 : 2 : 1$ (p. 121). In fact, they do not do so but give a whole gradation of forms due to the new combinations produced by the crossing in the many genes controlling them. These statements may seem to contradict Bateson's belief (p. 103) that species are differentiated by large and strongly marked non-quantitative characters. They do not do so, for the differences may often be large and strongly marked. He was however wrong in assuming that such differences are necessarily based on unitary hereditary factors. Most of them are based on summation of many small differences.

This new conception of the mode of action of the genotype in the body destroys the whole force of Bateson's criticism of the natural-selection theory. Selection is exerted on the organism's body, not directly on the hereditary material, the genotype; it is the characters as expressed in the body that come directly under the influence of selection, and in discussing selection we must consider its effect on them. If in a race of animals some character such as large size is advantageous, those individuals that have this character developed above the mean will be selected. These will be individuals in which the complex of genes controlling size is in a condition making for large size. They will have more offspring than the smaller animals and will hand over their larger size to the next generation, since the characters of all genes are inherited. The mean will therefore be greater in that generation, and this increase of size will continue from generation to generation until the largest mean size that the genotype is able to produce results; or until increase in size ceases to be advantageous.

In this process of selection it is favourable combinations of the genes already present in the genotype before selection began to act that are selected. It is no more than *re-combination* of the material present in the genotype at the start; no new hereditary characters arising during the selection have been considered. But mutations giving larger size may arise at any time during the process and these also will be favoured. Most of them will be in modifying genes of small expression, for differences in these genes are much more numerous than in the genes of larger expression. By these mutations larger changes may be produced under selection than would have been possible if the original genotype were unchanged. Occasionally perhaps a mutation in a gene of larger expression in size may appear. This also will be favoured.

Throughout the whole of this selective process, except when a mutation of large expression appears, the change in the population will be *gradual*; this is, as we have seen, a necessary result of the control of the character by a large number of genes, rather than by a single gene. It will also be *continuous* and *directional*, the change continuing in the same direction through many generations. There is also no reason why several distinct characters in the body should not be selected at the same time, so that the structure will alter simultaneously in all of them. Now, these were just the features that we found to be characteristic of evolution in nature where

K

we could directly observe it (p. 101). They are also the characters of evolutionary change which are demanded by the theory of natural selection and which Bateson was unable to account for on his views of the mode of action of the genotype. We may conclude that his criticisms have been answered and that the deadlock between the results of the geneticists and those of other biologists studying evolution, which seemed so absolute thirty years ago, has been resolved.

There are other requirements that our scheme must be shown to satisfy before we can say that the course of selection so outlined will unquestionably lead to evolution of the type that we observe in nature. This is so, even though we still restrict ourselves to the genetical side of the enquiry and to the small changes of micro-evolution, leaving the larger evolutionary changes to later consideration. Of these further requirements three may be considered.

1. When we were discussing the reactions of biologists to Darwin's publication of his theory, we noted (p. 51) that he discussed hardly at all how changes in the parts of the body could remain co-ordinated so that the organism retains its ability to function efficiently as a single whole. There is no doubt that such co-ordination is necessary; without change in other parts, any large change in one of the parts would result in the organism becoming inefficient and subject to removal by selection. If in a mammal increase in size is the character that is being selected, the legs must become stronger to bear the increased weight, and their muscles stronger if the animal's locomotion is not to be impaired. Changes will be required in many other organs. We have to ask how such co-ordinated change is provided for on the scheme that has been proposed?

Here the fact should be emphasized again (cf. p. 71) that if change is not great and sudden the organism is able to adjust itself during the life-history of the individual to altered demands on the organs. We see this in man and other animals. When muscles are much used they become larger and stronger; hair becomes thicker in animals exposed to cold, and thinner in hot conditions; if one lung is destroyed, the other becomes larger and may carry out the whole respiration of the body. These changes are immediate adjustments in the individual's body; they are phenotypic and are not inherited—they cannot therefore give rise to any evolutionary change. They are also limited in extent. But when some change is going on in a population under selection, and the change is not large, they will see to it that the animal remains efficient during the course of the evolutionary change. In the early stages of micro-evolution, when the changes are always slight, there should be no difficulty in understanding how co-ordinated change occurs in the body.

As the evolution proceeds and the changes required in other organs become larger than can be provided by this type of phenotypic adaptation, they can be produced only by recombination and mutation of the genes under selection in the same way as the original change with which they are co-ordinated was produced. At first sight it may seem unlikely that appropriate changes in many parts of the body would appear in a population when they are needed, so that they may be selected. But the variability of natural populations in genes of small expression is so great—the number of mutations in these genes are so many among the individuals of the population—that they provide material for selection in any direction in which it is required. The need for co-ordination will probably always make evolutionary change under selection slower than it would otherwise have been, but there is no reason to think that it should make it impossible.

The need for co-ordination may be otherwise stated by saying that the *genotype* in any organism must throughout a process of change be maintained in a condition to give an efficiently functioning organism. For this, co-ordination between the *genes* is necessary; only some combinations of genetic factors will enable the genotype to work together harmoniously to give an efficient organism. Such *harmonious co-ordination* in the genotype will be maintained by selection in all populations of organisms in nature. It will be regained after it has been disturbed in any way by change in the genotype. Recombination under selection and, later, mutations in other genes will be selected to give a new condition of harmonious co-ordination, from which the required efficiency in the functioning of the body will result.

It follows that the effect of mutational change when it first occurs is not necessarily the same as after the readjustment that returns the genotype to harmonious co-ordination. When it first occurs, a mutation may be of only slight advantage; its advantage may be much greater when the genotype is restored to genetic co-ordination. As Huxley has said:[1] 'The offer made by a mutation to the species is not necessarily a final offer. It may be merely a preliminary proposal, subject to negotiation. Biologically this negotiation is effected in the first instance by recombination and secondarily by mutation in the residual gene-complex. It can lead to marked alteration in the effects of the mutation, which may make the proposal acceptable to the organism.'

[1] J. S. Huxley, *Evolution: the modern synthesis*, 1942, p. 124.

2. In the scheme that has been outlined it is assumed that natural selection will be effective in causing the spread of an advantageous character through a natural population of organisms. When we were discussing the position of the theory of evolution at the end of the nineteenth century (p. 97), we noted that there was at that time no direct evidence for the efficiency of selection, and regarded it as one of the weaknesses of the position. We must ask whether the position today is any stronger in this respect. Is there now any more reliable evidence that natural selection is effective in nature?

We have reports of several instances in which mutations of large expression in the body have spread through natural populations. The dark varieties of butterflies in industrial regions, already mentioned (p. 133), give one example of this. The black form was probably present as a rare mutation before the spread began; the country was not then industrialized, and on the lighter background the mutation was disadvantageous and did not spread. With the darkening of the background that accompanied industrialization it became advantageous and spread rapidly, replacing the lighter form. If this is the true interpretation, selection was clearly responsible for the spread; selection was in this instance effective.

Another example is the spread of a dark variety of the hamster (*Cricetus cricetus*) in southern Russia. This variety has spread in the last two centuries over distances of hundreds of miles, replacing the normal form. Here the reason for the advantage of the dark coloration is unknown; there has been no industrialization to explain it, and it has been probably due to some advantageous character—possibly greater viability—associated with the coloration. But selection must have been responsible for the spread.

There is also some experimental evidence that varieties bearing mutations may be protected from attacks of predators, if the mutations give better resemblance to the background, and some experimental evidence dealing with other characters.

All this evidence, however, is concerned with mutations which produce large alterations in the body; for the small and often quantitative differences in which individuals in natural populations differ—and which we have supposed to be the chief material for the action of selection in the process of micro-evolution—we still have no direct and reliable evidence that selection is efficient in nature. It is hardly possible that such evidence should be forthcoming. It would be extremely difficult to collect it by observation—the period of observation would need to be very long and many observations would be needed if the results were to be reliable. To provide such evidence by experiment would be even more difficult.

It must be admitted that even today our belief in the efficiency of selection depends on logical deduction rather than on the results of observation or experiment. But it may be added that the logical basis of the belief is stronger than it was fifty years ago. It has been greatly strengthened by mathematical analysis of the conditions under which selection should be effective in natural populations, if it acts upon differences inherited in the Mendelian manner. Supposing there are no changes in the environment which would alter the force of selection while a character was spreading through a population, the mathematicians have been able to show that the character will spread if its selective advantage[1] is not smaller than $1/N$ where N

[1] By a selective advantage of $1/N$ it is meant that under selection $N + 1$ individuals bearing the character will survive for every N that do not bear it. A selective advantage of $1/1,000$ means that 1,000 individuals bearing it survive for every 999 without it.

is the number of effectively breeding individuals in the population. In large populations, with more than 1,000 individuals, this advantage is very small, far smaller than we could hope to demonstrate by observation or experiment. In smaller populations the necessary advantage is larger and selection will be less effective. We will consider the cases of small populations again later (p.148f).

We know by direct observation, for instance in palaeontological series, that populations of organisms do change with time in many characters; we know that individuals in natural populations vary and much of the variation is inherited; and we know from the mathematical analysis that, if the differences between the individuals are associated with small differences in selective advantage, they should be selected and spread. On the basis of this knowledge it seems an unavoidable conclusion that selection acting on the observed differences is the cause of the changes in the populations, that is to say of their evolution. There is no evidence opposed to this conclusion, and it therefore seems that belief in selection as an efficient agent in the production of evolutionary change cannot be avoided.

3. Lastly, there is a difficulty in our interpretation of genetical change in the evolution of organisms that has not yet been fully solved. In the genotypes of organisms as we find them in nature, most of the genes are in the dominant condition (p.110). But most of the mutations that arise in genotypes in nature are recessive. Does this mean that only the relatively rare dominant mutations (7 per cent. in *Drosophila*) are used in evolution?

We know that the condition of dominance or recessiveness of a mutation can be altered by change in other genes, just as other features of its expression can be altered by modification (p. 129). It has been suggested that, if an advantageous recessive mutation occurred, selection would see to it that the changes needed to bring it to dominance took place, for it would spread more rapidly as a dominant and this would be advantageous. It could then be received into the genotype of the race as a dominant.

This is the theory of the Evolution of Dominance (R. A. Fisher).[1] Its truth has been disputed on the ground that, when the recessive mutation was still rare soon after its occurrence, there would be no sufficient force of selection to cause this evolution of dominance. For the selection would act only when the mutation was expressed in the body and this would be only when two individuals bearing it mated, which would be excessively rare. The question has been much discussed but cannot be said to be finally settled. If Fisher's theory has to be given up, it would seem that we must look to the rare dominant mutations for most of the raw material of evolution, or to the evolution of dominance at a late stage of the spread of a recessive mutation.

In any complete discussion of the question whether our present conceptions of the genotype and its action on the body provide a suitable basis for micro-evolution as it is observed in nature, there are many other subjects that should be discussed. But these are less general and fundamental than those we have considered. It must be enough to say that our present evidence is everywhere in agreement with the belief that evolutionary change of the kind we observe in natural populations, both living and fossil, might be caused by selection acting on the variations we find in the populations, provided they are inherited according to the laws of Mendelian heredity. So far the theory of natural selection has indeed come

[1] *Amer. Nat.*, **62**, 115, 571, 1928; *Biol. Rev.*, **6**, 345, 1931.

into its own again, but this does not give us a complete understanding of micro-evolution. We also need to know the conditions in which populations of organisms are distributed in nature and to ask whether the natural populations are of kinds in which evolution such as our theory demands could occur. This is the subject of the next chapter.

CHAPTER 12

The Last Thirty Years—Ecology

RECENT discussion of the problems of evolution has paid more and more attention to the facts of the organism's life in its natural entironment, its ecology. This is a return to Darwin's position. He realized, as we have seen, that evolution takes place in the organism's natural life, and that any theory to account for it must take account of the conditions of that life; he based his theory on his experience as a naturalist. In the latter part of the nineteenth century and the first quarter of the twentieth, this outlook fell into the background. Biologists then were more concerned with the structure of organisms and their behaviour in the laboratory rather than in nature. It was left to those of the last thirty years to return to Darwin's outlook. We must now discuss the results to which their work has led.

The ecology of animals and plants differs greatly owing to their different characters as organisms. Plants lack the power of active movement that animals possess, and are unable to choose their mates for interbreeding— a very important point, as we shall see, in the discussion of micro-evolution. For these reasons the relations between their ecology and their evolution are essentially different from those of animals. The theory of micro-evolution has made much more certain advance in discussion of animals, and in this and the next chapter we shall mainly consider animals.

1. A very obvious fact about the distribution of animals —and plants—in nature is that they are distributed in

the groups that we call *species*. Roughly, the species of the biologist are equivalent to the kinds of animal or plant that the layman recognizes. In general each kind of organism is distinct from all other kinds; any individual can without difficulty be placed in its kind or species. This is not true in every instance, but there is no doubt of it as a general fact. In spite of this, definition of the characters that make it possible for the biologist to say that some differences are, and others are not, species differences has been a puzzle in biology up to very recent times. Darwin and the nineteenth-century biologists who followed him believed that the species difference is not essentially different except in size from the smaller differences that are found in the variation of organisms within a species. He believed that organisms differentiate gradually in evolution both below and above the species stage, which was no more than one point in a gradual sequence of change. Biologists, he thought, arbitrarily choose a stage of the differentiation as that at which they think the differences have become sufficiently marked to justify them in regarding them as specific.

Here, his views are not borne out by the work of recent naturalists. It is now accepted by most naturalists that species, at least so far as animals are concerned, are real natural groups; they are not artifacts of the biologists. They do not intergrade with each other as smaller groups often do; they are more permanent than any smaller groups; and when they are in contact they usually differ in details of their ecology, even though they may be closely related.

Thus, animals naturally occur in species groups. There has been much discussion about the characters which distinguish the species differences from the differences between smaller groups of animals, but it is now widely accepted that the real distinguishing feature of the species is that it is a group of animals or plants that normally interbreed together. Within the species, no matter how distinct infra-specific groups may be, interbreeding will occur if the groups come into contact; organisms do not *normally* breed with those of other species. This is not to say that hybrids between species cannot occur. Many species will hybridize in exceptional circumstances, as when breeding within the species is prevented, and the hybrids may be viable, but in their normal lives different species do not interbreed, being prevented from doing so not by its impossibility but by habit, mating preferences, and other similar causes. It may be that the definition of the species difference can be made more fundamental by saying that the species group is one within which a common communal life is possible, interbreeding being one aspect of that life.

This definition of the species difference is by no means without its difficulties. It cannot apply to animals that reproduce entirely asexually, without interbreeding, and it is not clear that the species is the same phenomenon in all animals, the simplest as well as the most complex, but, so far as the great majority of animals with bisexual reproduction are concerned, it seems to be very generally true. If so, the problem of the definition of the natural species is well on the way to being solved. In plants the position is by no means so clear. This definition cannot be applied to them, since they cannot live a communal life as a group, or choose their mates for interbreeding.

If the species difference can be so defined, it is clear that, from the point of view of the theory of evolution, the species stage of differentiation is a most important stage in the divergence of groups. Within the species intermixture of the genotypes will occur whenever two distinct forms interbreed, and the differences between them will usually be lost when this occurs (cf. pp. 155). Once interbreeding ceases, and the forms have become different species, this can no longer happen. Their differentiation cannot be lost except by the extinction of one or both the groups. From that stage onwards their evolution is independent.

2. Next, we must discuss the distribution of the individuals within the range of the species.

A naturalist, when he is looking for a species in the countryside does not look for it everywhere. He knows the type of environment in which it lives, and expects to find it only when he comes upon a locality which, by experience, he knows is suitable for it. It is indeed a general truth of natural history that species are not distributed evenly over the species range, but rather in small populations in localities where the conditions are particularly suitable. Some few wide-ranging species, such as far-flying birds on land or whales in the sea, may not be so distributed—they may perhaps be divided into no distinct populations smaller than the species—but it is certainly true that the vast majority of animal species are so distributed.

These local populations of a species vary enormously in size, from the small number of individuals that may inhabit a pool of water to the many millions of a shoal of herring in the sea or of a planktonic species in a lake. All intermediates between these extremes of size occur. Further, this type of distribution is as general in the common species as in the rarer; the common species is distinguished rather by the shorter distances that separate its local populations than by any lack of distinctness between the populations.

The local populations of a species are isolated from

each other more or less completely by the unsuitable environments that separate their localities. Here again there is very great variability. The isolation is probably almost complete between populations on islands separated by considerable stretches of water, or in isolated bodies of water on land. In many other cases it may be much less complete, but recent study of ecology has shown that the movements of many animals are much less than might be expected. Populations of field mice separated by a few hundred yards have been found not to mix; snails do not travel more than a few yards in a year; and even the birds in a wood have been found not to mix with those of another wood a mile or so away. In all these cases there is a very definite isolation between populations which are by no means distant from each other.

These local and at least partially isolated populations may be called *demes*.

It is in these demes that micro-evolution goes on. As soon as two populations are isolated, they will begin to diverge, either in adaptation to small differences in their environments, or because mutations that occur in one do not occur in the other. It is important to realize that complete isolation is not necessary for the evolutionary change in two demes to be independent. Mathematical analysis has shown that the spread of a mutation of selective advantage $1/n$ (p. 140, note) will be independent in two populations if the migration between the populations is less than $1/n$ of the effective breeding population in each generation. When the differences of selective advantage or the isolation are greater than this, the population will evolve independently. As we have seen (p. 141), the course of evolution will vary with the size of the population. Selection will be more effective in the larger demes which will therefore be more closely adapted to the conditions of their environments; smaller demes should be more variable. Whether in the smaller demes, mutations may spread which are entirely without selective advantage, i.e. are neutral so far as adaptation is concerned, has been disputed. Some think that spread of such neutral mutations is the cause of the presence of the many characters in organisms that appear to us to have no value in the adaptation of the organism.

3. Evolution, even micro-evolution, is a slow process, taking many generations to produce a noticeable change in a population, and changes in the geography of natural environments are not infrequent in nature. Only in rare instances will demes be sufficiently permanent to allow more than small evolutionary differences to develop in them. It is probably only in such environments as islands and isolated mountain tops that demes may remain indefinitely isolated. When that is so, the isolated deme will differentiate continuously until it becomes a new species. But it will be much more common that a deme which has evolved for some time in isolation will, owing to changes in the geography or environment, come into contact with another deme of the same species long before they have become specifically distinct. When this happens, interbreeding between the demes will occur, and (provided the differences between them are slight, p. 152ff) the two demes will fuse. Similarly, division of a deme by environmental change in a part of its range will be frequent.

We must then think of the evolution of a species which is distributed into demes in this way as taking place in a network of dividing and fusing demes. When two demes fuse the differences that they have evolved in isolation will not be entirely lost. The population formed by their fusion will be intermediate between the two original demes. Advantageous characters that have been evolved in either deme will be retained by the action of selection. This process of frequent fusing and splitting of demes will go on over the whole species range, so that advantageous characters will spread over the whole range. Any migration between the demes will also tend to spread the characters across the species range. The result should be that the species genotype is kept everywhere similar by transference of genes and that it should gradually evolve by accepting advantageous characters that have been evolved in the demes.

This is the general picture of the process of micro-evolution in a typical animal species that results from recent ecological work, but it must not be forgotten that the details of the process are undoubtedly greatly variable among the species of animals. Demes vary in size and in the extent of their isolation; some unusual species may not be divided into distinct demes; and in the rare species in which reproduction is entirely non-sexual, the whole process of evolution will be different. How they will evolve is discussed on a later page (p. 162).

4. The distribution of characters over the species range often shows types of regularity not so far discussed. Of these two must be mentioned.

(*a*) If the species range is large, the environmental conditions in its more distant parts may differ so much that the adaptations of the animals in these parts are noticeably different. Thus, in Russia, there is in the honey-bees a gradient in several characters, associated with the gradient in temperatures as one passes from south to north. Size is larger in the north, the tongue and legs shorter, and various other characters differ. Similar gradients over wide ranges have been found in the pigmentation of some birds, and in structural characters of some fishes, e.g. in the number of vertebrae in the Atlantic cod[1]. In some cases the variations have been shown to be hereditary, and not due to direct action of the environmental conditions during the life history. Gradients of this kind are known as *clines*. Sometimes the gradation is continuous and regular over the whole range, sometimes regions in which the characters change little are separated by others where the change is rapid. The first are known as *internal* clines, the second as *stepped* or *intergroup* clines.

In these clines the species will normally be divided into demes, and the gradation of characters is a gradation from one deme to another. Where the variations are hereditary, the gradation results partly from different adaptation in the parts of the range, selection changing as the conditions differ. It may also be due to incomplete diffusion of mutations across the large distances within the range. Diffusion of characters over a large distance is necessarily slow, for only animals close together can mate, and many matings are needed to transfer a character far across the range. Thus, complete fusion of characters everywhere in the range will be prevented, and the force of selection in the different parts of the range will maintain the differences. Stepped clines are due to constancy of conditions or easier interbreeding in the parts where the characters change little, and the opposite of these conditions where the change is rapid.

(*b*) It may often happen in the course of the evolution of a species divided into demes that, as the result of some change in the environment, a deme or a group of demes becomes completely isolated from the rest of the species. Land may become separated as an island, an area of forest separated from other forest areas by the

[1] Schmidt, J., *C. R. Trav. Lab. Carlsberg*, **18**, 1, 1930.

L

development of grassland or desert between them, an arm of the sea may be cut off from the open sea. If the isolation is complete, the isolated part of the species will evolve independently. It will begin to diverge as soon as the isolation becomes complete and its divergence will continue so long as the isolation is maintained.

We must distinguish this *divergent* type of evolution (which on a small scale occurs in the demes of all species that are divided into demes) from the evolution of a population living without isolated parts and evolving by closer adaptation to the conditions of the environment and to any changes that occur in it. This latter type of evolution may be called '*successional*'.

When a geographically separated part of a species becomes sufficiently different to seem to biologists to deserve a separate name, but is still able to interbreed with the rest of the species, and is therefore not a new species, it is called a *subspecies*. This is clearly no more than a temporary stage in the divergent evolution of a separated part; subspecies will in time, if the isolation is maintained, sooner or later become species.

The rate of evolution is slow; periods of 100,000 or 1,000,000 years are often given as typical of the time required to evolve a new species, though the rate is extremely variable. Environmental changes will occur frequently in such periods, and it will often happen that subspecies which have become differentiated will be brought into contact again as the result of some change in the environment. If they are still subspecies, they will then interbreed, and it might be expected that they would necessarily fuse into a single population, characters being transferred from one population to the other by the interbreeding. Observation seems to show that this does not always take place. We know of many pairs of subspecies that have been in contact for many years and show no signs of fusion although they interbreed freely. They may form viable hybrids which are capable of reproduction for one or more generations, and yet the parent forms remain distinct.

It is possible that the frequency of these cases may be due in part to the fact that we are living in an exceptional period of the world's history. The retreat of the ice at the end of the Ice Age took place only a few thousand years ago, and must have resulted in great environmental changes in temperate latitudes. It may be that some of these pairs of subspecies have not yet had time to fuse and that they ultimately will do so. But, however this may be, there are reasons for thinking that fusion is not the inevitable result of the meeting of differentiated forms within a species.

The hybrid between two forms that have become considerably differentiated is in general weaker than the parent forms. This is because the two forms during their differentiation will each have evolved in their genotypes a system of 'harmonious co-ordination' (p. 138), and these systems will have come to differ from each other as the differentiation went on. When the two forms interbreed, the hybrid genotype will be a mixture of the parent genotypes and will lack the co-ordination of either. Since the effect of the co-ordination is to enable the genotype to produce an efficient organism, the hybrid will necessarily be less efficient. Its weakness will be proportional to the extent of the differentiation in the systems of co-ordination in the parent genotypes, and thus to the extent of their divergence in isolation.

(In parenthesis, it may be mentioned that this effect is the opposite of the 'hybrid vigour' often observed when an inbred stock of a domestic animal, such as the cow or the horse, is crossed with another stock. The hybrid is then often found to be more vigorous than the parent inbred stock. The cause of the difference in the two effects lies in the greater similarity of the genotypes when inbred stocks of domestic animals are crossed. Two stocks of horses or cows are much more closely related than subspecies in nature; their genotypes will be much more similar, and crossing will cause little disturbance of the systems of co-ordination in the genotypes. The offspring of the cross will therefore not show any significant weakness. That, on the contrary, it may show improved vigour is due to an effect of close inbreeding. We have seen (p. 132) that the individuals of animal populations normally differ from each other in the numerous micro-mutations that they carry. Most of these are harmful, but they are recessive and will remain in the heterozygotic condition (p. 115) unless the same mutation is carried by both the parents of a mating. So long as they are heterozygotic, they will not affect the bodily condition of the offspring, but, if the interbreeding is close, the parents will more often carry the same mutations, and these will then become homozygotic and weaken the offspring. Crossing with another stock, which is unlikely to carry the same mutations, will bring the mutations back to the heterozygotic condition and therefore restore the strength of the stock.)

To return to the results that follow meeting between well-differentiated populations such as subspecies. Production of weak and relatively sterile hybrids is necessarily wasteful to the species; they will decrease its efficiency in competition with others. For this reason individuals within each population which do not hybridize with the other population will be favoured by selection, since they will leave more efficient descendants than those that do. Mutations that make hybridization more difficult, and therefore reduce the risk of it, will be favoured, so that hybridization will decrease and the populations tend towards the condition of distinct species. The meeting, in fact, will lead to more rapid differentiation of the populations to the species stage than would have occurred if they had not met.

We have then two opposed tendencies that may follow the meeting of differentiated forms. If they are slightly differentiated and the hybrids not significantly weak, they will tend to fuse by transference of mutational differences from one to the other across the zone of hybridization, where the two forms meet. Not only single demes but some subspecies are likely so to fuse. If the forms that meet are originally more strongly differentiated, isolating mutations will be favoured by selection and the forms will diverge to become separate species more rapidly than if they had not come into contact. It is not possible to say in any specified case which of these tendencies will prevail, but it is clear that we ought not to expect meeting always to lead to fusion of subspecific forms. It may often lead to more rapid differentiation, and in some cases the two tendencies may be so nicely balanced that neither fusion nor rapid differentiation takes place and the forms remain unaltered, so far as we can see, for long periods, although they interbreed and produce viable hybrids. Thus, our unexpected observations of examples in which this seems to occur are explained.

This account of micro-evolution in the natural conditions of animal ecology has been very summary. In a complete account many other phenomena that occur in the natural lives of animals would have to be considered. Such are the rhythms of population number that occur in many species, as in those which are populous in the summer and reduced to small numbers in the winter, or others which vary rhythmically in number from year to year; polymorphism, the occurrence of two or more different forms in the adult of a species; mimicry and protective resemblance (cf. p. 179) and many others. All these have their different effects on the course of micro-evolution, but they are not general to all, or even the majority of species, and we have not space here to discuss them. This however is clear. The ecology of organisms is as variable in its details as we found the genetics to be, and the course of their micro-evolution will vary in each species with the details of both its ecology and its genetics.

CHAPTER 13

The Course of Micro-evolution

THE conceptions of genetics and ecology developed in the last two chapters have been various and somewhat complex. We may now see how well they fit together to give us a general picture of the course that micro-evolution is likely to follow in a typical animal species.

Suppose we have a deme of some bisexual animal, let us say horses or antelopes living on a grassy plain or fishes in a lake, and suppose that the deme is sufficiently isolated from other demes to allow its independent evolution. The deme will then undergo successional evolution in this environment. Differences between the individuals will be selected, and those better adapted, since they will leave more descendants, will tend to determine the characters of later generations. Adaptation should improve. In this process both recombination and new mutation will take part. Since most of the differences between individuals of a population are micro-mutational, having small and quantitative effects on the characters of the body, the evolution will consist mainly of gradual changes in the relative sizes of the parts of the body, though changes in physiological and other characters may occur. All parts of the life-history, the developing young as well as the adults, may so alter. Throughout this evolution the genotype will be maintained in a condition of harmonious co-ordination, so that the animals remain efficient.

Occasionally a mutation of larger effect may appear. This will probably be recessive and will only be expressed in the body when two individuals bearing it mate. If it is advantageous, its spread is sure, unless it is lost by the chance death of the individuals bearing it, but the spread at first will be very slow. At some point of spread it may, however, be modified to dominance and it will then spread much more rapidly.

The successional evolution of the deme will continue so long as its isolation is maintained and the conditions of the environment are unaltered. But environments are always changing, though their changes are often slow. The deme will continuously re-adapt to the changed conditions. Most of its re-adaptation will consist of quantitative modification dependent on micro-mutational change, but larger mutations which have previously been rejected may, if they occur again, be advantageous in the changed conditions and be accepted.

Successional evolution is always slow, except in changing environments, taking as much as one million years to produce differences that the systematist may regard as specific. Re-adaptation to changed conditions may lead to much more rapid evolution.

It is evolution of this type that we see in the faunas of palaeontological series of strata.

In all this evolution the deme is likely to diverge from similar demes in other environments. This will be partly because the changes in two environments are unlikely to be exactly the same, and partly because mutations which occur in one deme do not occur in another.

Suppose now some major change occurs in the environment of our deme. Perhaps, it is invaded by a group of predators against which the animals of the deme must defend themselves, or, perhaps, their food supply fails and they are forced to resort to other food. The first and immediate response will be phenotypic modification of the animals' bodies in association with their changed habits. If the deme is one of horses or antelopes and a predator appears, legs will become longer and stronger and the animals will become more alert; if a change in food-supply is necessary, alterations in the physiology of digestion may be required. These changes will happen during the individual's life, and will not be inherited. In the next generation recombination will start. Combinations of genes better suited to the new conditions will be favoured and their effects will supplement those of the phenotypic modifications.

In succeeding generations recombination will continue, the genotype always tending to approach the combination of genes most suitable for the conditions. At any time new advantageous mutations may appear and will tend to spread under the action of selection, slowly if they are recessive, more rapidly if they are dominant when they appear or become so later. Most of these new mutations will be micro-mutations but some may be of larger effect. Some perhaps will be only slightly advantageous when they first appear but may become much more so as the result of further recombination. Their effects will always be added to those of recombination, and may result in larger adaptational change than recombination alone could produce. Throughout, harmonious co-ordination within the genotype must be maintained.

By modifications of these types the deme may be able to survive even large changes in its conditions of life, provided the changes are not so great and rapid that it becomes extinct before it has had time to re-adapt. It will diverge from other demes of the species throughout its period of evolution in isolation. If its isolation is continued for sufficient time, a single deme may become a new subspecies and even a new species, if it diverges far enough to prevent interbreeding with the rest of the original species.

Much more often our deme will either become extinct or, as the result of some environmental change, come into contact with another deme of the species before its differentiation has proceeded far enough to prevent interbreeding or even to make the hybrids that result from interbreeding significantly weaker than their parents. The two demes will then fuse by transference of the genetic differences between them across the zone of hybridization. The fused deme will be intermediate between the two fusing demes. In the fusion advantageous characters of both demes will be preserved.

During the long periods required by evolution, even micro-evolution, fusions of demes will occur frequently, and equally frequently demes will become divided into parts by changes in their environment. So long as the occasional fusion and splitting of demes occurs without break over the whole range of the species, characters evolved in the isolated demes will diffuse throughout the range. The genotype of the species will everywhere be kept similar by transference of characters at the repeated fusions, and will evolve by taking into itself new advantageous characters which have arisen in the demes. Only if the distances across the range are large enough for the conditions in its distant parts to be markedly different, so that selection acts differently in the parts of the range, may the diffusion of characters over the range be unable to counter-balance the differences due to adaptation in its different parts. We then find the species arranged as a cline, with a gradation of characters from one end of the range to the other.

When the species is thus evolving as a whole, either

with the formation of clines or without any clear differentiation over its range, its evolution as a whole is successional. But if groups of demes become completely isolated from the rest of the species by environmental change that separates their locality from other parts of the range, they will undergo divergent evolution during their isolation, just as isolated demes do. Then, they may diverge far enough to become separate subspecies, and the species will come to consist of a group of these subspecies. Finally, the subspecies may become new species, if their isolation is continued long enough.

Subspecies that have evolved in this way may come into contact as the result of further environmental change. What will happen then we have discussed in the last chapter. If their previous differentiation is slight they are likely to fuse; if they are considerably differentiated, they will diverge at an accelerated rate to the species stage; and it is possible that these two tendencies may be in balance so that they remain unchanged in spite of interbreeding and hybridization.

So we are able to give a reasonably clear account of how micro-evolution will proceed in a typical bisexual animal species, and our account is consistent with all our knowledge of the heredity of animals and of the conditions of their life in their natural environments. In detail the process will vary from one species to another; we can never predict how it will proceed in detail for any one species. But our conclusions are founded on a wide basis of knowledge, and it is not likely that they will be found in the future to be wholly fallacious, though they may well be modified in the light of further knowledge.

Even if this account is sound for the micro-evolution of the majority of animal species, it must not be assumed that new species do not arise in nature in other ways. It has already been pointed out (p. 144) that the ecological differences between plants and animals prevent conclusions derived from study of animals being directly transferred to plants; the micro-evolution of plants needs separate discussion, which it is not possible to give here. It is also clear that our scheme of micro-evolution cannot apply to the rare animal species in which reproduction is not bisexual. A non-sexual species divides into a large number of lines, called *clones*, each descended from a common ancestor, and these clones then adapt to the particular environment in which each is living. When the clones meet, they cannot interbreed but they come into competition with each other and the best adapted survives. Here, there seems little difficulty in understanding the course of micro-evolution.

Another question that has raised discussion is whether in any circumstances such differentiated forms as subspecies and species can arise within populations of the original form, without the geographical isolation which we have assumed in discussing their origin. It is clearly possible for an isolating mutation to appear within a population, that is to say a mutation that makes it impossible for the individual bearing it to mate with the normal form of the population. But if such an individual is to mate, and so to prevent its mutation being lost, it can only do so with another also bearing the mutation. Mutations of the same kind are very rare (one in 10^5 or 10^6 individuals, p. 118), and the chance of two individuals with the same mutation meeting would be almost negligibly small. It is therefore often concluded that origin of differentiated forms without isolation is very unlikely.

Perhaps, this argument is not so inescapable as it seems at first sight. Mutations are usually recessive when they first arise and are not expressed in the heterozygotic condition. In that condition a mutation that is isolating when expressed would not prevent mating with the normal form. The mutation would only become homozygotic and expressed when the two mating individuals both carried it, but if there was close inter-breeding in the population, the chance of this happening would be considerable. For in a small group of individuals many heterozygotes of the mutation would be produced, and, if these mated, the result would be that several individuals of the isolated form would be produced in close proximity to each other. By mating together these might give rise to a population of the new form within the original population, and among this new population the isolated form could perpetuate itself, if it were better adapted. Periods of asexual reproduction alternating with sexual reproduction might give the same result. We have no evidence that evolution of this kind occurs in nature, and it can in any case be no more than an occasional method of species formation. It is not likely to be common.

There may be other ways in which species are evolved among animals. But it certainly seems that the type of micro-evolution that has been discussed in the major part of this chapter is the most general among bisexual animals and may be regarded as the normal type.

CHAPTER 14

The Larger Course of Evolution

THE theory we have discussed in the last three chapters seems to give us a reasonably satisfactory understanding of the small changes of micro-evolution. But even a complete theory of micro-evolution would be only a first step towards understanding of evolution as a whole. To understand micro-evolution is important for any general discussion of the problems of evolution, for there can be no doubt that all evolution takes place on a background of micro-evolution. Organisms have always lived lives similar to those they now live, and it is presumably true that micro-evolution has always gone on in much the same ways as we have found it to go on today. We have to ask in this chapter whether this is all there is to be said about the larger changes of evolution. Can we believe that the whole course of evolution results from long-continued micro-evolution of this kind and nothing more, that no other evolutionary processes are involved? It is not difficult to see that other causes of change might be important in large-scale evolution, though we have not met them in our discussion of micro-evolution. They might be too rare to appear in our observations and yet common enough to have important effects in the long periods during which evolution has been going on; or they might need longer periods to develop their effects than those in which micro-evolution takes place.

The vertebrates are the animal group that offers us the best opportunity of studying evolution on a large scale. Their whole evolution from primitive fishes to the mammals has taken place during the period of the fossil-iferous rocks, so that we have fossil evidence of its whole course; and their hard internal skeleton is suitable for fossilization with the result that their evolution is better recorded in the fossils than that of any invertebrate group. We may then be well advised to look mainly at the facts of vertebrate evolution. At the same time we must remember that the vertebrates have been an exceptionally successful group of animals. It must not be assumed that the evolution of the many less successful groups is in all ways similar to theirs.

What are the most outstanding general features of the course of evolution in the vertebrates when it is considered as a whole?

1. We find that during the evolution of the vertebrate several successful types of vertebrate organization have been evolved one after the other. There were several such types of fishes, and, later, the amphibians, reptiles, birds and mammals have followed. As soon as one of these types became successful, it split up to form a varied fauna consisting of parallel branches adapted to many modes of life within the broad environment of the group. Horses, cows and deer, monkeys, bats, whales and so on are examples of these radiating branches of the mammals. Mammals radiated in this way in the Tertiary period—the last sixty million years of palae-ontological time—and the birds at almost the same time; reptiles radiated in Secondary times—150–60 million years ago—and before them the Amphibia; and there were several radiations of fishes. Each of the radiating groups was dominant in its environments during the period of its radiation, and during each radiation the type which was next to radiate evolved by modification

of the previous radiating type. We find, then, two types of evolutionary change occurring during vertebrate evolution, radiations of successful types of vertebrate organization and evolution of new types of organization during each of the radiations. There is evidence for evolution of a similar kind in some of the more successful groups of the invertebrates. We will consider these two processes of evolution separately.

2. In the radiation of a successful group of vertebrates, most of the changes in evolution are brought about by change in the size of the body as a whole and in the relative sizes of its parts. In terrestrial animals there is often a general increase in size as this evolution goes on though this is by no means universal—reduction of size may occur in some lines. Thus, horses increased in size from that of a dog to that of the modern horse; elephants and many other groups of mammals similarly got larger. So did many of the reptile groups. The changes in *relative* size of the parts during the evolution occur in very many of the organs of the body. In the horses legs became longer, the middle toes were enlarged and the side toes reduced to splint bones, so that the animal came to walk on a single toe, the face became longer and the teeth high-crowned for grinding (Fig. 3). Nor did the evolution take place in a single line. Throughout the radiation the line of descent continually branched, only a few of the side branches surviving to give rise to the animals of later periods.

One of the clearest characters of this radiating evolution is that it is everywhere adaptational—it is therefore often called *adaptive radiation*. When they first became dominant, the mammals were small terrestrial, running animals, some of them arboreal, leading in fact the type of life that the least specialized

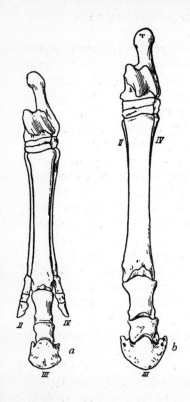

FIG. 3. Hind foot of (*a*) three-toed Miocene horse (*Protohippus*) and (*b*) modern horse, to show reduction of the outer toes to splint-bones (After Scott).

mammals, such as many of the insectivores, lead today. From this type they spread to the various habits of life that mammals follow today—the flight of bats, the marine life of whales and porpoises, the fossorial habits of many rodents and some other groups, and so on. The radiation is, in fact, a divergence of the branches to occupy all the niches open to mammalian life within the environments of the mammals as a whole. Adaptation to the conditions of the mode of life that each

M

branch has adopted is everywhere apparent in the specialization of its structure.

3. The evolution of a new type of vertebrate organization from the type that preceded it—that of the birds and mammals from the reptiles, the reptiles from the amphibians, or the amphibians from the fishes—occurs by modification of one of the radiating lines of the previous radiation. During reptilian radiation the mammals thus arose from the synapsid reptiles and the birds from another reptilian group, the dinosaurs, not closely related to the synapsids. This type of evolution occupies long periods—40 million years in the cases of both the birds and mammals. That it should need these long periods is not surprising, for the re-organization needed to produce a new type of vertebrate is much more fundamental than any that takes place in the radiation of the branches in adaptive radiation. Every part of the body is reorganized both in structure and physiology, and many new organs are evolved. In the mammals, mammae, sweat glands, the diaphragm, the placenta, control of temperature and warm-bloodedness are all characters that have no counterparts in the reptiles. If we also remember the complexity of co-ordinated change required in other parts when any considerable change occurs in a part of the body, the long periods needed for evolution of this type should not be surprising.

We have far better evidence of the course of evolution in the origin of the mammals from the reptiles than of any other of these large re-organizations in the vertebrates. We have numerous fossils of the synapsid reptiles that show us many stages in the evolution of mammalian organization, and in the monotremes—the duck-bill platypus (*Ornithorhynchus*) and *Echidna*—we have surviving examples of a mammalian stock which probably diverged in Triassic times. They give us indications of the condition of the soft parts and physiology in the very early mammals of that period. Both the synapsids and the monotremes are highly specialized to their peculiar modes of life, but it is not impossible to discount their specializations and to deduce the course of change by which mammalian organization was evolved.

When we do this, it appears that the various characters of the mammals were evolved successively, not simultaneously. In the synapsids modifications of the teeth into incisors, canines and molars and of the limbs for locomotion in the mammalian manner, which is much more efficient than the reptilian manner of using them, were early steps in the process. The synapsids from which the mammals evolved were fast-running, carnivorous reptiles and these changes were adaptive to their habit of life. Other steps towards mammalian organization were later added to these, probably as further improvements in the same type of adaptation.

We have far less good evidence of the course of evolution of the other major vertebrate groups. Between the birds and the reptiles we have only a single fossil form, *Archaeopteryx*, sufficiently intermediate to show us many of the steps of the evolution. But there is no reason to doubt that a new type of organization was evolved by essentially the same process in all examples, in the vertebrates and probably also in many groups of the invertebrates. This process differs from that of adaptive radiation not only in being a much more fundamental reorganization of the body but also in the evolution of many more new organs during its course. Change in the relative sizes of the parts of the body occurs continually in both types of evolution, but here it is not so clearly the dominant form of change as it is in adaptive radiation.

4. Two other general features of vertebrate evolution must be mentioned. First, the evolution of the vertebrates has been a continuous invasion of new environments, in each of which, as they spread into it, they become dominant. The earliest vertebrates we know were mud-grubbing, bottom-living fishes; they evolved to become free-swimming fishes inhabiting all layers of the water, actively swimming after and catching their prey; then in two steps, as amphibians and reptiles, they invaded the land; as the birds they became aerial and as mammals more efficient terrestrial animals. These were only the largest moves in their successful progress; between each of these were many invasions of more restricted habitats.

Other successful groups of animals spread during their evolution in much the same way. Insects, spiders and other arthropods invaded the land from their original aquatic habitats; the land snails among the gastropod molluscs did the same; and many animal groups have passed into the fresh waters from the sea. Spread from one habitat and one mode of life to another is characteristic of successful evolution.

A second feature of successful evolution illustrated by the history of the vertebrates is progress towards the development of 'better' organization, that is towards a condition in which the animal becomes capable of a more efficient life and greater independence of the conditions of the environment. Among the vertebrates there can be no doubt that the mammal is much more efficient, a much 'better' animal in this sense, than a fish; it is capable of much more elaborate behaviour and of living healthily in a much larger range of environmental conditions. On similar grounds it must be admitted that the insect is a better animal than the worm-like ancestors from which the arthropods evolved. One of the most valuable features in this progress is evolution of greater power of maintaining conditions within the body constant in spite of change in the external environment. Migration to a terrestrial environment always makes this isolation more easy, and in the birds and mammals it was further improved by evolution of a constant internal temperature.

To say that the later-evolved forms are 'better' animals is merely to say that evolution is progressive, and the progressive character of all successful evolution cannot be questioned. We find this progress not only in the evolution of single groups such as the vertebrates or the arthropods but also in the whole course of animal evolution from single-celled forms upwards. It is true that all animals that survive today are efficient in so far as efficiency is necessary for their survival, but as we pass from the simpler to the more complex forms we find that the animals come to be less and less at the mercy of their environments, more certainly able to choose the conditions in which they live and to ensure their reproduction, and their behaviour becomes more and more complex. They become more efficient organisms.

Yet it must not be forgotten that progress of this type is not a universal character of all evolution. Relatively few animal types have evolved progressively so as to give rise to more advanced later forms. Most of the invertebrate groups—the coelenterates and planarians, for example—have not, so far as we know, given rise to any higher forms in the very long periods since they were evolved. They have continued to live the life to which they are adapted, and have survived without essential change. Even in the progressive groups many of the earlier types survive—for instance fishes and amphibians among the vertebrates, and the mono-tremes among the mammals. It is, in fact, one of the most surprising features of palaeontology that it shows us so relatively few major groups of animals that are extinct. Progress of the kind we have defined is character-istic of animal evolution when considered as a whole, but this results from the progress of a few groups. We should probably regard progressive evolution as an occasional episode in the history of all animal groups, for even the groups that we now regard as backward must have arisen by evolution of this type when they were first evolved; they differ from the groups that we call progressive in that their evolution has ceased to lead to more advanced forms. Sometimes, indeed, they may show little change of any kind through very long periods; there are animals such as the brachiopod *Lingula* which are hardly at all different from their predecessors of the earliest fossiliferous times. Many of our bivalve molluscs, such as the oysters, are very little different from the forms of two hundred million years ago.

After this summary of the general features that evolution on a large scale shows, we may pass on to ask how far it is in accordance with the conclusions that we reached in discussing micro-evolution and whether it raises problems that we did not meet in that discussion. There are many features of these larger changes of evolution that we should expect as the result of long-continued micro-evolution. It is to be expected that a progressively evolving group should under the influence of selection show continually changing adaptation to the conditions of its environment, and that it should spread into new environments whenever it was able to do so. The type of change that we found to be so prevalent in adaptive radiation—change in the relative sizes of the parts of the body—is in accord with the quantitative changes due to micro-mutation that we found the dominant type of change in micro-evolution. It is also to be expected that the internal organization of the body should be improved under the influence of selection, so that progress in the sense we have defined it should result. But there are some features of evolution on this large scale that do not so readily fit in with our account of micro-evolution. These must be discussed.

1. We often find change continuing in the same direction in a group of animals through very long periods. Increase of size in the horses or the elephants continued from the Eocene to the Pleistocene, some 60 million years. There were other such continuing trends in these groups, and similar trends are equally evident in many other groups. If increase of size is beneficial— and there is evidence that it often is in terrestrial animals—and if evolution can, as we have seen (p. 152), only be slow, it is to be expected that selection towards increased size would continue for a considerable length of time and that the size should gradually increase. It should do so until a point was reached at which further increase of size was no longer beneficial, which is bound to happen sooner or later, for no animal can become indefinitely large. That point was in fact probably reached in the Pleistocene horses and elephants.

There is then no difficulty in understanding change in the same direction going on for some time under the influence of selection acting continually in the same direction—often called *ortho-selection*. But we should, at least at first sight, expect selection to produce the optimum size in much shorter periods than those during which these trends continue in evolving animals. We know that in artificial selection of domestic animals changes of size almost as large as those which occurred in the evolution of these groups can be brought about within a few thousand years, whereas the natural evolution took 60 million years and several million generations. It is true that natural selection is probably not in general as powerful as that which man applies, and it is also true that much co-ordinated change in many parts of the body is necessary to keep the animal in a viable state for its life in nature, probably much more than is necessary to keep it viable under the protection of man.

Still, the very long periods of these trends of change has seemed surprising to many biologists, and the suggestion has been made that they are not solely due to orthoselection, but that we must postulate some inherent character in the animals causing them to evolve in this direction and not in others. Evolution controlled by such inherent tendencies is known as *orthogenesis*. If such control existed, it would introduce an entirely new principle into our theory of evolution.

The opinion of biologists is almost universally against the necessity for demanding any inherent orthogenetic tendencies to explain these long-continued trends; the evidence is clearly against the need for postulating them. For one thing the trends are not universal in the groups which in general show them. Some minor groups of horses evolved to smaller and not larger size, apparently in adaptation to special conditions of their life. If the reversal of the trend in these groups is adaptive, it suggests that the trend towards larger size in other horses was also adaptive. In any case, an inherent orthogenetic tendency would surely be present in all members of the line of descent of the horses, and not reversed in a few of them.

There is one way in which an inherent character may to some extent control the direction of evolution in animals. If the only mutations that occur lead to certain types of change, and none to others, it is clear that evolution will be possible only in these directions. We sometimes find similar characters in several related species within a genus, and it is possible that this may be due to the same mutations occurring in all these species. This would be a true inherent tendency controlling the evolution, but it certainly could not be responsible for the long-continued trends that we find in palaeontological evolution.

The probable explanation of the trends is ortho-selection continued throughout the period of the trend, and the reason why this selection does not produce more rapid results is the very complex co-ordination in many parts of the body needed to allow the trend to continue. This may not be the complete explanation, but at least these trends do not seem to require us to postulate inherent orthogenetic tendencies controlling the course of evolution.

2. It is not at first sight easy to understand how animals that have become adapted to one environment and mode of life are able to change it for another. This has happened, as we have seen, often in the evolution of the vertebrates; fishes became terrestrial in the amphibians, reptiles aerial in both the birds and the pterodactyls, mammals aquatic in the whales and

porpoises, and aerial in the bats. Nevertheless, though large changes such as these have occurred many times in vertebrate evolution, they are not frequent in the history of a group; vertebrates have only once become terrestrial, and only three times aerial. Smaller changes of habit, as for instance change from one food plant to another, are much more frequent. We know examples of such changes in living animals, for instance in animals which have become pests on crops having previously fed on uncultivated plants.

A large change of environment and habit requires much reorganization of the body. An animal specialized to one mode of life could not, one would think, change it for another without much co-ordinated change in its body. If it passed to a new mode of life in a new habitat, it would be likely to meet competition from the fauna already present in the new environment and adapted to it. It would be unlikely to survive.

In part this difficulty is answered by the fact that such large changes must have always taken place in many steps. Fishes migrated to the land from stagnant and shallow freshwater environments, probably through the stages of aestivating in the mud when the pools dried, active amphibian life during the period of aestivation, and so on. Birds at first developed their wings as organs for gliding from tree to tree, and only later learnt to use them for active flight. Since small changes are not difficult, it may be that a series of them might without difficulty give rise to one of these large changes. But a series of small changes, if it were to lead to a large change, would have to be accurately correlated with evolution in new characters of the body as it progressed. This may perhaps have occurred in the infrequent cases in which animals have succeeded in making large changes of habit, and be one reason why they are not more frequent.

It has also been suggested that large changes of habit would be easier if the adaptations evolved for the original life happened to be useful in the new life. Such *pre-adaptation* could only happen by chance and would therefore not happen often, but since the large changes of habit are themselves infrequent this is not a serious objection to the view that pre-adaptation has been valuable in their evolution. We have in fact some evidence of its occurrence. Fishes probably evolved air-breathing lungs while they were still aquatic, and in adaptation to the lack of oxygen in the stagnant waters they lived in and the consequent inefficiency of their gills. They may also have modified their fins into primitive legs for walking among the vegetation above the mud at the bottom of the water. We know of a few other examples in which there seems to have been pre-adaptation.

In these, and perhaps other, ways it may have been possible for animals to evolve even such large changes of habit as migration from the water to the land.

3. One of the most surprising facts of evolution is the fantastic development of certain organs, often to a state in which they seem necessarily to be disadvantageous to the animal. The feathers of the birds of paradise, the peacock's tail, the horns of the Irish elk—10 feet across from side to side (Fig. 4)—and the very heavy protective armour of many of the large Secondary reptiles are well-known examples. Surely, it may be said, the over-development of these organs should have been prevented by selection before they reached this size.

Here, it must first be noted that, at least in living species, these organs in their present condition are not

FIG. 4. Horns of Irish Elk.

harmful enough to prevent the survival of the species that bear them. Also, they all have their uses, often in sexual display and fighting, sometimes for protection. They may in some cases reduce the animal's powers of locomotion but they are certainly useful in these other ways.

Probably the apparently excessive development of some of these organs is due to linkage with another character, such as the size of the body as a whole. The horns of the Irish elk are probably an example of this. The elk was a very large deer and had clearly evolved towards large size. Now, we know that the growth of horns in deer is more rapid than that of the body as a whole, that is to say that as the animal grows bigger the horns grow relatively bigger. If increase in size is advantageous—as it normally is in terrestrial animals—and if this linkage cannot be broken, we should expect increased size to be favoured by selection until its advantage was balanced by the disadvantage of excessively large horns. At that stage the horns would be above their optimum size and might seem to us over-developed in size and even fantastic, but the size of the body would be less than what would be its optimum without horns.

This explanation will not cover the development of all these organs; many of those used in display are not obviously associated with evolution of increased size, or, as far as we know, any other character. Nevertheless, the cause of their development may be somewhat like to that of the horns of the elk. If an organ is used in sexual display with the function of stimulating the female to mating —the usual function of display (p. 77)—it will probably serve its purpose more effectively the more elaborately it is developed. Selection will favour development of these organs and will continue to do so until they become so large or elaborate that they reduce the animal's efficiency in other ways. There will again be set up a balance in this case, between the advantage in display of elaboration in these organs and their other disadvantages. In the balanced condition they may seem to us over-developed.

4. The extraordinary facts of mimicry and protective resemblance have often been thought to raise difficulties for any theory of evolution in which characters are believed to have been gradually evolved by accumulation of small additions. It has been said that in the early stages of their evolution, when the resemblances must have been very incomplete, they would not have deceived a predator and therefore would have been of no selective advantage.

The answer to this objection is similar to that given (p. 75) to the objections to a gradual evolution of complex organs such as the vertebrate eye. We saw that this argument concerning the eye neglects the evolution of function. In the early stages of its evolution the eye was valuable since it served much simpler functions for which complexity of structure was not required.

The evolution of the resemblances of mimicry and protective resemblance would be no harder to understand than that of the eye if it could be shown that the incomplete resemblances from which they must have originated would be of value. Here the recent results of study of the behaviour of higher animals such as the birds—which are the most important predators of the insects, the animals in which the majority of these resemblances are found—help us towards understanding the evolution. It has been found that birds and other animals in many circumstances recognize objects not by their general appearance as we do, but by whether they possess some one or a very few characters—called valent characters. All the rest of the characters of the object are neglected. Thus, a male robin recognizes another male by the red feathers of its breast, and will attack a few breast feathers if they are put up in its territory on a stick, not distinguishing them from another living robin. This in spite of the absence of all other parts of the body. Hudson found that house-martins recognized a cat that they were accustomed to attack by the colour ond texture of its grey coat, and would equally attack his cap which was of about the same colour and texture. All other characters of the cat were unimportant for the stimulation of the reaction. Not all animal behaviour is of this simple type but the fact that much of it is helps us to an interpretation of the evolution of mimetic resemblances.

It is not unlikely that a resemblance in some one character that was valent for an important predator might arise by chance between an animal and another well-protected species. This would be of value in warding off the attacks of the predator. But predators are usually of many species, and the different species will probably use different valent characters. The protection will be increased if the resemblance can be extended to these other characters. Thus under selection the almost complete resemblances that we observe between mimics and their models might be built up.

The evolution of protective resemblance would be similar. An originally simple resemblance between an animal and a non-living object would be protective if the resemblance was in a character that was valent to some predator searching for food. By the addition of more such resemblances, valent for other predators, elaborate examples of protective resemblance might be built up.

We are thus able to see that the evolution of these phenomena, astonishing as many of them are in the completeness and detail of the resemblances does not offer any unavoidable difficulty to a theory of evolution based on the gradual accumulation of small differences. It is in showing us how very incomplete resemblances may be of selective value that the modern study of animal behaviour is here so useful.

5. Lastly, there are problems raised by the element of progress in evolution. These are the most fundamental of all, for it is the progressive nature of biological evolution, its progress from the simple to the complex, towards a 'better' organism and more 'efficient' life (p. 170), that is the most outstanding characteristic of evolution in living nature. In micro-evolution we see how organisms change in their characters as the result of selection acting on the variation that occurs in them, and in adaptive radiation how these changes can accumulate to give the differences we observe in the various members of such large groups as the mammals or reptiles. But evolution is more than variation within a single type of organization. There is also in it, as we have seen (p. 7), progress

which has led from the single-celled Protozoa to the higher vertebrates and the flowering plants. More elaborate structure and more complex functional differentiation of the parts of the body, better co-ordinated physiology, more varied behaviour, and greater independence of the conditions of the external environment all play their parts in this progress.

We cannot believe that evolution has been merely expression of characters present in organisms from the beginning but unexpressed in their bodies until the later forms were evolved. Any such *pre-formation* theory of evolution is today unthinkable in view of the enormous complexity that we know the organism's body to contain. The single cell of the protozoan cannot contain within itself all the hereditary characters required not merely for the organization of the mammalian body but for that of the bodies of all the predecessors of the mammals in evolution. But if preformation cannot be accepted it is clear that complexity of organization in organisms must increase in evolution; there must have been a true evolution of *new* characters, an adding of new characters as evolution proceeded. We find no evidence of this in our studies of micro-evolution, where change is nothing more than alteration of characters already present, probably because our observations cannot be continued over a long enough time. These novelties occur, as we have seen (p. 169), occasionally during adaptive radiation, and are much more frequent in the large steps of evolution, such as those that gave rise to the origin of the mammals or the birds from the reptiles. They were probably at least equally frequent in the earlier evolutionary steps such as those which led to the origin of the vertebrates from their invertebrate ancestors, or the evolution of many invertebrate phyla from their simpler ancestors. The larger the evolutionary change we are considering the larger part evolution of new characters seems to have played in it.

It is necessary to make quite clear what is meant here by novelties in evolution. In addition to alteration of the characters of an organism by such processes as change in relative size, we often find in the larger evolutionary changes that organs become so far altered in their general characters that superficially they seem new organs. Frequently it is only study of comparative morphology that shows us that they were in fact evolved by modification of organs already present. Thus, the larynx of the mammal can be shown to be derived from the gill-slits of the fish and their skeleton; hair in mammals and feathers in birds are probably derived from reptilian scales. There are also other types of evolutionary change that should be regarded as modifications of characters already present in the body. Alteration of the location of an organ in the body, reduplication of an organ, in a segmented animal change in the number of segments, and still other types of change, should be so regarded.

None of these are novelties in the sense used here. They are all modifications of elements of organization previously present in the body. It is the necessity to demand new elements added *ab initio* to organization in the course of evolution that we are discussing, that is to say new elements added to the organization of the body as new formations and not arising in any way by modification of previously-present differentiations. It is true novelties of this kind that increase of complexity seems to require.

As an example of a true novelty in evolution, we may take the horns of mammals. Some evidence of the way in which they arose is given by the palaeontology of such

N

a mammalian group as the titanotheres. In that group the horns appear first as slight thickenings on the previously undifferentiated surface of the frontal bones of the skull; they appear where there was no previous differentiation to be modified into them. Later, these thickenings grow out to form horns, presumably by the normal evolutionary process of change in relative size. New organs seem often to arise as at first small differentiations which later grow larger by change in relative size.

Can the theory of evolution we have developed give us any basis for understanding how these novelties are evolved? Our theory of heredity is based on the genes as being the carriers of the hereditary factors of the body, and genes are now generally believed to produce their effects by controlling the nature of the enzymes present in the body. The character of the body at the various stages of its life-history are, very largely at least, controlled by the actions of its enzymes and so are ultimately under the control of the genes. Mutation is either a change in the chemical nature of a gene, and so of its enzyme, or a change in the arrangement of the genes in the chromosomes, which also results in modification of the action of the gene.

If mutation, which is the only form of hereditary change of which we have definite evidence, is always change in genes already present, it would at first sight seem that we have here no basis at all for understanding the evolution of novelties in the organization of the body. For their evolution we surely need new hereditary factors, not change in those already present. But we must remember that conditions in the body and in the hereditary material are extremely complex. Possibly changes in the distribution of enzymes in the body, if they were somehow brought about, might cause new differences in rate of growth of parts, as, for instance, in a part of the frontal bones of the skull resulting in the early evolution of horns. It is hard to see how redistribution of its enzyme could be brought about by mutation of a gene, but, in view of the complexity of the conditions in the body, it may perhaps be possible. Also, it is not impossible that new genes may be evolved. We know that genes may be reduplicated within the chromosomes, and, when that has happened, one member of such a pair might become so altered by mutation as to give us what is functionally a new gene.

These suggestions are purely hypothetical. For the present we cannot say more than that novelties of organization undoubtedly occur in evolution; that they are essential to the increase in complexity which is associated with progress in evolution; that we have no accurate knowledge of the details of their evolution. But we may perhaps add that it seems possible that changes of the kind that we know to occur in the genotypes of organisms may give rise to these novelties as well as to other types of evolution.

The origin of novelties is not the only feature of progressive evolution that needs interpretation. It may be asked why progress occurs so markedly in some lines of descent but not in others. Why did the very large amount of re-organization necessary for the evolution of the mammals occur in the synapsids, or that required to evolve the birds in a single line of dinosaurs, whereas all the other reptile groups, though they radiated strongly, still remained very clearly reptiles? There must have been some reason for the much more fundamental evolutionary change in these two groups and not in the others. Why, again, do many whole phyla of animals remain unprogressive while others progress?

We have not yet any satisfactory answer to these questions. Other, similar gaps in our knowledge might be mentioned.

These are some of the problems that are raised by the facts of large-scale evolution. We cannot directly observe evolution on this scale, and our solutions of its problems are therefore bound to be to a large extent hypothetical. Nevertheless, that such explanations are possible may confirm our belief that our theory of evolution is at least broadly sound. We have not found it unavoidably necessary to postulate any new principles to explain the phenomena of the larger course of evolution.

CHAPTER 15

Conclusion

IN the first chapter it was said that our discussion would not include either the earliest or the latest stages of evolution. At both its ends, the origin of the first living organism and the development of man's societies since he became self-conscious and able to control his progress by tradition, the problems raised are so different from those of evolution between these limits that they certainly deserve separate treatment which cannot be given to them here. Our discussions have been concerned only with the middle course of evolution. They have led to the theory of evolution that has been sketched in the last four chapters.

Our theory is founded on the Darwinian conception of natural selection as the directive force guiding the course of evolution. It may therefore truly be called neo-Darwinian. Indeed, it is surprising how few of Darwin's views have been shown by later work to be unfounded. In a few pionts he was mistaken. For instance, his belief in blending inheritance has been definitely shown to be wrong, his acceptance of Lamarckian inheritance as playing some part in evolution has not been confirmed, and his opinion of the nature of the species differs from ours. Also, his theory of pangenesis, which he put forward as no more than a hypothesis unsupported by observation, is not now accepted. But these points are few. Our theory is derived from Darwin's; it is a development of his theory modified as the study of biology has proceeded. It is an advance on his theory, being based on a much wider knowledge of natural history and heredity; in the main it has not advanced by replacement of errors in Darwin's beliefs.

Our theory is by no means complete; there are many gaps in it which can only be filled by further study and greater knowledge. Naturally, these gaps are less in our interpretation of the smaller evolutionary changes, for we are able to study these more directly than we can the larger changes. It may indeed be said that we can now understand fairly clearly how the small changes of micro-evolution are brought about, and that the gaps in our interpretation of it are not very important. Nevertheless, there are gaps even here. One of the most unfortunate is that our knowledge of the extent of close inbreeding in natural populations of animals is so slight. More knowledge of this would help us to esti-mate more certainly the rate of spread of variations, the effectiveness of selection and the likelihood of evolution of non-adaptive characters. It would also help us to decide, whether it is possible for non-inter-breeding varieties to arise within continuous popu-lations without geographical separation. It is hard to believe that all the nearly related species that we now find living close to each other in the same environment have differentiated in separate environments and later come together again. Groups of as many as fifteen such species in contact with each other have been described. It would be much easier to understand their evolution if it is possible for a species to divide while still forming a continuous population. These are not the only gaps in our knowledge of micro-evolution, but on the whole the others, like these, are concerned with detailed phenomena and not with the process of micro-evolution as a whole. In its main outlines our theory seems now well established.

When we try to interpret the larger course of evolution, we cannot, since we are unable to observe its progress directly, do more than state its probable causes. We can show that most of the changes we find are such as might be produced by long-continued evolution of the kind that we have found to be effective in micro-evolution. There is little difficulty in doing this for many of the features of large-scale evolution, but we have seen that there are still gaps in our interpretation. The most important gap is undoubtedly our lack of knowledge of how novelties of organization—in the sense that we have defined them (p. 183)—arise. They are essential to progress in evolution, and it is the progressive character of biological evolution that most clearly distinguishes it from any phenomenon in non-living nature. It will be a major task for future study of the process of evolution to decide the manner in which they are evolved. Biological evolution results first from the power of organisms to perpetuate themselves by handing on from one generation to another the system of control necessary for the co-ordination of the organisms's life, secondly from the organisms's ability to change in form, and, thirdly, to progress with time. Given the power of perpetuation, which we know all organisms to possess, and given our present knowledge of the means by which changes of form are brought about, we could broadly understand the whole course of evolution if we knew the means by which it is able to acquire novelties of organization and so to move towards greater complexity.

This, at all events, seems to be the appreciation of the present position with which most evolutionary biologists would agree, except that many way not feel so keenly this difficulty in accounting for the evolution of novelties of organization on the lines of our present theory. They would say that it is not impossible that the kinds of variation we know may give rise to these novelties and so to increasing complexity and to progress. That is true. They would also say that until it is shown that other principles are required, we have no cause to question the adequacy of the theory.

Still, even if our theory is capable of accounting for all the facts we observe in our study of evolution, it does not necessarily follow that organisms never evolve in other ways. So far as much of evolution is concerned, our theory can only be put forward as a possible and, we may think, probable explanation, not as demonstrable truth.

There have always been biologists, and are still some today, who are not so completely satisfied with the neo-Darwinian theory. Probably the most frequent critical outlook is based on the belief that our theory pays too little attention to the active nature of the organism; that it neglects, at least so far as animals are concerned, their power of reacting actively, of choosing their environments and so of controlling their evolution to some extent. This criticism has been mentioned earlier (p. 87) in connection with the neo-Lamarckians. It has greater weight the higher the animals whose evolution is being considered, until in man the power of controlling his evolution has become so great that natural selection has almost ceased to direct it. But all animals have some power of choosing their environments and so of modifying the action of selection. Any neglect of this power is certainly a weakness in our theory. This is a criticism that has always been levelled against the Darwinian theories, and it must be admitted that it still seems to have weight.

Partly, this neglect of the active nature of the organism has been due to the fact that the emphasis in discussions of evolution has, since Darwin's time, always been on structural change rather than on evolution of other characters of the organism. Perhaps, the Darwinian theories owe some of their surprising success to this relative neglect of the evolution of the more active characters of the organism. If so, this alone would be enough to show that the explanation of evolution given by our theories is incomplete.

Partly, again, the neglect is due to the fact that we have very little knowledge of the heredity of behaviour. We know that instincts are inherited, and in a few examples, mostly such pathological examples of behaviour as waltzing in Japanese mice, we know that they are inherited in the Mendelian manner. We have very little knowledge of how the instincts that control the behaviour of animals' natural lives—those of display, nest-building and song in birds, for example—are inherited. More knowledge of the heredity of habit and instinct, and more discussion of the parts they play in evolution would greatly help our theory, for there can be no doubt that they have been important in controlling the course of evolution.

It is possible that another direction in which our present theory may be modified in the future is by return towards Darwin's belief that Lamarckian heredity plays some part in evolution. The present discredit of the Lamarckian assumption that acquired characters are inherited arises from our inability to see how changes produced in the body during the life-history could induce changes in the genotype which will give rise in the bodies of the next generation to characters similar to those acquired by their parents. But it is always unsound in science, and especially in biology, to say that an effect is impossible because we cannot see how it could be brought about. The conditions in nature are too complex, and we know them too incompletely, for such judgements to be justifiable. In the history of science they have often been confounded by later discoveries; Kelvin's denial that the solar system could be more than a few million years old is one classical example, and Bateson's denial of the possibility of evolution being directed by natural selection is another example.

There are phenomena in evolution which some believe to suggest that, whatever may be said against it, there is some truth in the Lamarckian theory of inheritance, and it is possible—one does not want to put it more strongly than that—that in the future truth may be found in it, and the neo-Lamarckians so far justified. Its role in evolution could never be more than subsidiary for there are many facts that it could never explain— the facts of protective resemblance and mimicry are obvious examples—and we know that very many of the changes we find in direct observation of micro-evolution are not related to habit.

There are other directions in which increased knowledge would greatly help our understanding of evolution besides those that have been mentioned— the mode of inheritance of habit and the extent of inbreeding in natural populations. Some others may be mentioned here.

1. The part that co-operation both within species and between species plays in the life and evolution of

animals deserves more study. Darwin's emphasis was entirely on competition and he has often been criticized for neglecting the opposing principle of co-operation. We know that the living together of individuals or species for their common benefit is a real and common fact of nature. Species often associate for reasons of protection, for advantages in gathering food or for other reasons; within species social communities are formed and are clearly of advantage to the species. Until recently this subject has been very little studied, but in recent years work on it has been done by a few zoologists (e.g. Allee[1]). There can be no doubt that it would repay further study. We should like to know how the evolution of animals is influenced by the phenomena of co-operation. Does it result only in closer adaptation to narrow and specialized modes of life, or are there more subtle ways in which the evolution of animals that show co-operation differs from that of those that do not?

2. There is the whole subject of the relations between animals and the conditions of their environments. Here it must be admitted that our knowledge is still very incomplete, and several lines of study are open. For instance, we know that the distribution of climate in the world has varied greatly from time to time during the geological past. Formation and removal of ice-caps, changes in the distribution of land and sea and of ocean currents, elevation and denudation of mountain ranges have all modified the distribution of climate. We have not much accurate knowledge of the extent of these climatic variations, and very little of the ability of animals to adapt to them. How has the evolution of animals been affected by these changes? At first sight it might seem probable that the more genial periods between

[1] E.g. W. C. Allee, *The Social Life of Animals*, n.d.

crises of mountain building or glaciation should be periods of evolutionary advance, and the crises predominantly periods of destruction of animal forms. But is this really so? It is possible that periods of difficult conditions may, on the contrary, be favourable to evolutionary advance. There is some evidence that difficult conditions resulting in occasional destruction of all but small minorities of the animals alive at the time lead to rapid change and rapid evolution.

There is another subject concerned with the interactions between the animal and its environment that may be mentioned. It has already been noted (p. 171) that the course of evolution seems to differ fundamentally in different groups of animals. In some, the progressive groups, change is comparatively rapid; in others there may be very little and even negligible change over long geological periods and in a few cases even over the whole course of evolution known to us from fossils (cf. Simpson[1]). Is this due to inherent differences in the animals—perhaps, lack of mutations in the slowly evolving forms—or is it due to differences in the relations of the animals to their environmental conditions? The latter is more probable. Simpson suggests that animals that evolve slowly live in relatively stable environments, and have reached conditions of equilibrium with their environments in which almost any evolutionary change is deleterious. More work on this problem, and on the whole subject of the rates of evolution under different conditions would be valuable.

3. Lastly, further study of the parts that the physiology and biochemistry of animals have played in evolution is likely to be very valuable. This subject has

[1] G. G. Simpson, *Tempo and Mode in Evolution*, Columbia University Press, 1944.

been discussed by Pantin[1]. The processes essential for the life of the organism were evolved very early; they are present in the simplest organisms alive today (cf. pp. 8-9). The essential metabolism of the cell has been varied and elaborated in later evolution, but it has not been fundamentally altered. Pantin points out that it consists of the large number of chemical and physical devices which form the subjects of the investigations of the biochemists and physiologists. It is from these initially-given intracellular processes, and almost wholly from them, that the more complex physiology of the higher organisms is built up. Throughout evolution they are preserved as units, so that its course seems to him like the building of a large number of models with the pre-formed units of a Meccano set. If this is so, evolution cannot lead to all imaginable results; its course must be determined, at least so far as the physiology and biochemistry of the body is concerned, by the properties of the materials it uses and the changes they can undergo. We saw (p. 173) that there is no evidence that inherent, orthogenetic principles control the changes of form that occur in evolution, but here is another way in which the inherent properties of the organism may modify the course of evolution and limit its results. At least, it is clear that more knowledge of physiological and biochemical evolution would greatly help progress towards a complete theory of evolution.

It is always rash to predict the future in science, and it may well be that our theory of evolution will progress on lines very different from these. However this may be, the study of evolution is actively advancing and will continue to advance in one direction or another. Of

[1] C. F. A. Pantin, Presidential Address to Section D, *British Assn., Advancement of Science*, **8**, 138, 1951.

this there can be no doubt, and any account of such a subject can never be more than an interim report. The theory will be modified as knowledge advances, and we may hope that it will become more complete, but even in its present condition it seems so well established in its broad outlines that it is unlikely to be fundamentally altered. It has advanced throughout the whole century since Darwin wrote, but its present form is based very largely on the rapid advances of the last thirty years which have given us new and accurate knowledge of many revelant branches of biology, especially genetics, ecology and the action of selection.

Our final conclusions must be (1) that, in the century since Darwin wrote, the truth of the occurrence of evolution has been so incontestably established that it is no longer in dispute in the general body of biological opinion and has not been for the last fifty years; and (2) that our present neo-Darwinian theory gives a reasonable and probably true interpretation of very many of the facts of evolution, and that there is good hope that those of the facts that cannot yet be interpreted may be explained by future development of the theory. But there is certainly much work still to be done before the theory approaches completeness.

THE GEOLOGICAL TIME-SCALE

Period						Approximate time since beginning of period (million years)
QUATERNARY						
Pleistocene	..	..	..	..	..	1
TERTIARY						
Pliocene	..	..	..	..	..	12
Miocene	..	..	..	..	..	30
Oligocene	..	..	..	..	..	50
Eocene	..	..	..	..	..	60
Paleocene	..	..	..	..	..	70
SECONDARY						
Cretaceous	..	..	..	..	..	120
Jurassic	..	..	..	..	..	150
Triassic	..	..	..	..	..	185
PRIMARY						
Permian	..	..	..	..	..	220
Carboniferous		..	..	..	..	280
Devonian	..	..	..	..	..	325
Silurian	..	..	..	..	..	350
Ordovician	..	..	..	..	..	400
Cambrian	..	..	..	..	..	500
PRE-CAMBRIAN	..	..	..	..	..	—

GLOSSARY

Adaptive radiation: the evolution of a successful group of animals by splitting into divergent sub-groups each adapted to a different life and habitat.

Amnion: a sac filled with liquid within which the embryos of reptiles, birds and mammals develop.

Brachiopoda: the lamp-shells, one of the smaller invertebrate phyla.

Catastrophic theory: the theory that the geological history of the world has consisted of a number of epochs separated by catastrophes in which all life was destroyed. Life was supposed to be re-created at the start of each epoch.

Chromosomes: rod-shaped bodies in the cells of animals and plants. They are of definite number in each species, and contain the genes in definite arrangement.

Cline: the type of distribution of a species in which the characters vary in a gradient across the species range.

Clone: a group of organisms descended from a single parent by non-sexual reproduction.

Continuous variation: the type of variation in a population of organisms in which the individuals vary quantitatively in the measurements of their characters.

Co-ordination in the body: the necessary inter-relations of structure and activities between the parts so that they may work together to give an efficient organism.

Curve-of-error: the distribution about a mean value when, in each of a number of trials, the result of each trial is determined by chance differences from the mean, as in the proportion of heads and tails obtained in repeated trials of spinning a number of coins.

Cysticercus: a bladder-like stage in the life-history of a tape-worm.

Deme: a local, partially-isolated population of organisms.

Diaphragm: the septum separating the thoracic and abdominal cavities in mammals, the midriff.

Dicotyledons: one of the classes of the higher (flowering) plants.

Dinosauria: a group of Secondary reptiles from which the birds were evolved.

198

Directional change: change continuing in the same direction over a period of time.

Discontinuous variation: variations, often large and qualitative, occurring rarely in a population and without intermediates between the variational and the normal forms.

Divergent evolution: the evolution of two groups of organisms which come to differ in isolation from each other.

Dominant: the condition of a mutated gene when it produces the same effect in the body whether it is in the hetero- or homozygous state.

Echinodermata: the invertebrate phylum that contains the sea-urchins, starfishes, etc.

Ecology: the study of the life of organisms in their natural environments, scientific natural history.

F_1, F_2, *etc.:* the first, second, etc., hybrid generations in an experiment in which different forms of an animal or plant are crossed.

Flagellata: a group of single-celled organisms characterized by possession of rhythmically contracting hair-like processes, the flagella.

Fluctuations: variations in the bodies of individual organisms due to differential action of environmental conditions upon them during the life-history. Sometimes also used in the sense of continuous variation in general.

Gamete: one of the two cells—eggs and sperm—that fuse at fertilization to form the zygote.

Gemmule: hypothetical particles supposed by Darwin to pass from the organs to the gonad and so to the next generation, where they are supposed to control the characters of the organs. See Pangenesis.

Genes or hereditary factors: units of the heredity of an organism, carried in definite arrangement in the chromosomes, stable through many generations, and together responsible for determination of characters in the body.

Genotype: the assemblage of genes in the heredity of an organism.

Gonad: the reproductive tissue of the organism from which the gametes arise.

Harmonious co-ordination: the co-ordination within the genotype that is necessary for efficiency in the organism.

Hereditary factor: see Gene.

o

Heterozygote: the condition of the organism in which a mutation is present in the gene derived from one parent but not in that from the other, and is therefore present in only one of the pair of genes in the genotype.

Homozygote: the condition in which a pair of genes are equivalent, either both bearing a mutation or both without it.

Hybrid vigour: the increased vigour often found in the hybrid between two, not too distantly related, stocks of the same species.

Incomplete dominance: the character of a gene in which the heterozygotic organism differs from either of the homozygotes and is usually intermediate between them.

Lycopods: a group of the flowerless plants including the clubmosses.

Macro-evolution: evolution of larger differences between organisms than those which separate species.

Marsupials: a subclass of the mammals in which there is almost always no placenta and the young are carried after birth in a pouch.

Micro-evolution: evolution up to the specific stage of differentiation.

Micro-mutations: mutations of small effect in the body, in modifying and other genes.

Modifying genes: genes whose only known effect is modification of the action of other genes.

Monotremes: primitive mammals that lay eggs—the duck-billed platypus, *Ornithorhynchus,* and the scaly anteater, *Echidna.*

Mosaic theory: the theory that each organ of the body is controlled by one or a few genes acting upon it and on no other organ.

Mutation: originally, a heritable alteration in the form of the body of an organism; later, a change in a gene resulting in alteration in its action in the body.

Natural selection: selection in nature of more efficient varieties, since these alone will survive in the struggle for existence.

Natur-philosophie: the transcendental zoology of the early nineteenth century aimed at finding a common plan behind the diversity of living organisms.

Neo-Darwinian theories: modifications of Darwin's theory taking into account the results of more recent work.

Neo-Lamarckian theories: theories based on the essential assumption of Lamarck's theory but developed more recently.

Organism: a fully effective member of the animal or plant kingdom.

Orthogenesis: the theory that the direction of evolution is determined by inherent characters of the organism and not by conditions outside it.

Orthoselection: natural selection continuing in the same direction over periods of time.

Pangenesis: the theory suggested by Darwin to explain Lamarckian inheritance. Each organ was supposed to contain particles (gemmules) differing in their nature with the characters of the organ, including those acquired during life. These passed through the gonad to the body of the next generation and determined the characters of its organs.

Parthenogenesis: development of an egg without fertilization.

Phanerogams: the higher or flowering plants.

Phenotype: the characters expressed in the body of the organism. They are due partly to the genotype and partly to action of environmental conditions on the organism.

Phylogeny: the study of the course that evolution has followed.

Phylum: a large sub-division of the animal kingdom. All the animals within a phylum should have the same fundamental structure.

Placenta: in the development of the placental mammals, an organ consisting of maternal and embryonic tissue in close apposition, through which the embryo is nourished.

Placental mammals: a subclass of the mammals in which a placenta is aways present.

Polyphyletic origin: the conception that a group of animals of similar structure, e.g. the mammals or birds, have been evolved from more than one ancestral stock.

Pre-adaptation: chance correlation between the adaptations required before and after a change in the mode of life, so that those evolved before the change are adaptive to the conditions after the change.

Pre-formation in evolution: the theory that the characters of later forms are present in the heredity of earlier forms though not expressed in their bodies.

Primary effect of a gene: its most obvious effect, by which it is usually named.

Pterodactyls: a group of Secondary flying reptiles.

Recapitulation: the theory that evolution advances by addition of new stages at the end of the development of the individual.

Recessive: the condition of a mutated gene when its effect in the heterozygote is the same as that of the unmutated homozygotic gene. Cf. dominant.

Recombination: the formation under selection of new combinations of genes in the genotype from among the varying combinations present in a population of organisms.

Saltatory evolution: evolution by large steps and not by accumulation of many small changes.

Segregation: the separation of the two members of a pair of genes in the formation of the gametes before fertilization. As a result, each gamete contains one example of the gene, not two as in the cells of the body.

Soma: all the tissues of the body except the reproductive tissue or gonad, i.e. the tissues responsible for the continuance of the organism's life.

Species: one of the categories of biological systematics. In bisexual animals the species may be defined as a group of animals capable of a common communal life, and therefore of normal interbreeding.

Sport: an early term of the same meaning as 'mutation' (q.v.).

Struggle for existence: the competition, within species or between them, that results from the excessive reproductive powers of organisms and the limited resources of natural environments.

Subspecies: a geographically-isolated differentiated group within a species. Subspecies are the largest divisions of a species, and a group is not given a subspecific name unless it is clearly differentiated from other parts of the species.

Symbiosis: living together of animal species for their mutual advantage.

Synapsida: the group of Secondary reptiles from which the mammals evolved.

Transcendental school of zoology: See natur-philosophie.

Uniformitarian theory: the theory that conditions on the earth's surface throughout geological history have not been greatly different from those of today, and that no catastrophes have occurred. Cf. Catastrophic theory.

Valent character: a character of an object that stimulates an animal to react in some way.

Vitalism: the doctrine that the organism's characters and activities are controlled by some guiding principle or vital force different in its nature from the materialistic forces of non-living nature.

Zygote: the cell that results from the fusion of the gametes at fertilization, the earliest stage of the life-history.

INDEX